Go Up &

Work with GOD

By
Vianna Stibal

Acknowledgements

The author wishes to express her sincere appreciation to the following individuals whose help was invaluable in creating the first publication of Go up and Work with God: Guy Stibal, David Reading, Barbara Hughs, and Iris Ann.

And a special thanks to my mother, Lorene Wayne Smith, for her diligent efforts and love in editing this second publication.

IMPORTANT NOTICE: All the information contained in this book is intended for educational purposes only. It is not the intention of the author to diagnose or prescribe.

First Publication: 2000
Second Publication: 2002
Other books by Vianna: Go Up & Seek God

Published by
Rolling Thunder
2935 East 400 North
Roberts, Idaho 83444
(208) 524-0808
email: vianna@srv.net

ISBN 0-9671754-1-0

DEDICATION

This book is dedicated to my God, Creator, Source, healer of the Universe. It was under Divine Direction that the information contained in this book was received, and by Divine Love and Healing that I was able to write this text.

To my mother, who taught me to pray and to believe that God always hears and answers our prayers.

To my husband, whose support throughout the writing of this book, and his assistance during my travels to teach these techniques to others is appreciated so much more than I could ever express.

To my children, who are now seeking their own paths in life, and learning some of life's difficult lessons.

To my precious grandchildren, who have each one, in their own unique way, brought blessings and joy to my life.

And to all the wonderful people throughout the world who have been a source of joy to me in my journeys to present these important techniques and ideas to the world. And to those that I have yet to meet. May your paths lead you to the place of greatest peace and abundant goodness.

And to Dave, whose friendship I cherish.

Preface 5

Forward 12

Chapter One-Basic Readings & Healings 14

Chapter Two-Why People Don't Heal 33

Chapter Three - Belief Systems And How to Change Them 39

Chapter Four-Gene Replacement 77

Chapter Five - Poisons & Toxins 86

Chapter Six - Vitamins & Minerals 92

Chapter Seven - Dealing With Illnesses 102

Chapter Eights - Guardian Angels 132

Chapter Nine - Waywards, Spirits, Psychic Hooks & Implants 136

Chapter Ten - Animals 142

Chapter Eleven - Indigo Children 144

Chapter Twelve - Soul Mates 148

Chapter Thirteen-Manifesting 153

Chapter Fourteen - My Little Story 158

Preface

For those of you who have not read my first book "Go Up and Seek God", let me give you a brief history of who I am and how this new book came about.

My name is Vianna Stibal and I am a medical intuitive. I was born intuitive, although I didn't start exploring my full poetential until later in life.

Because of health problems, I began studying Taoism, nutrition, and herbology.

In 1991 I was trained as a nuclear security guard for a local nuclear government facility. After receiving my training, I ended up working at a nearby manufacturing plant. On our breaks I would draw sketches of employees and give them short intuitive readings.

Because I was a single mother of three children, I soon decided that this was definitely not the right career for me. I began concentrating on my naturopathic training, and in March of 1994, I went into a full time naturopathic and massage business.

A friend of mine mentioned it might be a good idea to incorporate intuitive readings on the side for extra income. Since I already had the office and a growing clientele, I began booking readings.

Immediately, this part of my business began to succeed. Soon I had more clients for readings than anything else. I worked as both a personal and medical intuitive, receiving validation many times from the clients that I was working with.

My knowledge of nutrition was helping people, and I found that if I would listen, the Creator would give me instructions during my readings.

It seemed quite natural for me to look inside people's bodies, and even more amazing to me, I found I could observe the disease and affected areas of the body very easily.   I became quite good at the readings and was asked to do classes on the technique I was using.

Prior to this time I had developed a severe problem with my right leg, causing it to swell at times to twice its normal size. Due to the inflammation and severe pain, I decided it was wise to seek medical help. In August of 1995,

I was diagnosed with bone cancer. I was informed that I had a tumor in my right femur, and every test that they performed, confirmed this to be true.

The bone specialist told me that he had seen only two other cases like mine. He also informed me that he felt amputation might be my best option. This, he said, would give me a little more time to live. He sent me to the University of Utah for a biopsy. This procedure required that my leg be opened allowing the doctor to go in and scrape my femur for a sample. This ordeal put me on crutches and I suffered excruciating pain for about six weeks.

I was told that if I walked on my leg, it would break,and there would be no alternative but to amputate it to prevent the spread of cancer. I was also informed that I might only have a couple of months to live. I did not believe that this could possibly be happening to me.

My life seemed to be falling apart. I was in constant pain, hobbling around on crutches, but I still continued to see clients. This was not because I had great endurance, but because my family needed to be fed and I had financial obligations that needed to be met.

Even though I was newly married, the marriage was anything but a true partnership. Many healers heard of my plight and came from everywhere to help me. Some were wonderful healers, which I am sure kept me going through the dark times. I still thank God for Alice and Barbara for helping to take away the pain. I would also like to thank all those who prayed for me and helped me with love during this period. Still, I remained very ill.

I began cleaning out my body with lemon cleanses and sauna cleanses. I spent hours in the sauna; four hours a day for over two and a half weeks. I took vitamins and minerals and I prayed. Through it all, I still believed the diagnosis was wrong.

When the biopsy performed by the University of Utah came back, it came back negative and the doctors were confused. Every MRI showed that I had a tumor in the bone. The Mayo Clinic reviewed the test, and this time it was determined I had Lymph cancer. This diagnosis I believed to be correct.

I also believed mercury poisoning had caused my illness. Why? Because when I went up and asked God, I was told that it was mercury poisoning. The problem was, I didn't know how to get it out of my system, so I began digging for answers. I continued with my cleanses, always trusting the information that I got from Source. And even though I was sick, I continued to become more and more accurate with my readings. I knew that God could heal in an instant. I remember crying to God and asking why I was dying and losing my leg? I had too much left to do,

Since all my life I've believed I have a higher purpose, I sent forth a plea to the Creator. I heard a voice, loud and clear, as though someone was standing right next to me in my empty room, "Vianna you are here with or without a leg, so deal with it." Although I was shocked at hearing this, I still believed that with the Creator's help I could fix my leg; I just had to remember how to call upon God. However, the answer was with me all the time. It took an incident with my aunt to show me the way.

One day my aunt was very sick with the flu. She was in pain and had body aches. I went out the top of my head through my crown chakra, as I would do when giving a reading. I entered her space, and asked the Creator why she was sick, and I was shown. I then commanded the Creator to eradicate the pain in her stomach, and within in seconds the pain was gone.

The next incident occurred a couple of days later when a man came into my practice with a severe backache. Reflecting on what had happened with my aunt, I repeated the same procedure on him, and instantly his back pain was gone.

I decided to see if I could perform this healing technique on myself. I went up as though I was doing a reading on myself, and commanded my leg to be healed and my cancer to be gone. And it worked! My leg, which had atrophied and lost three inches in length because of the biopsy, returned back to its normal size. The pain was subdued and my leg was healed.

Today my femur is healthy, all tests are normal and I am free of lymphatic cancer.

I was excited about my own healing and I decided to use this procedure with all my clients. I found that the healings were becoming extremely successful with clients that I already had, and soon new clients, who were very

sick, were coming from all over the world. Many of them were healed instantly; others took a few sessions, and there was still others who did not heal.

While doing these healings, we felt very strongly that our brain waves were going into theta and delta. Thanks to a friend, who was a physicist and who "built' me an electroencephalograph, we were able to prove it.

There are four major frequencies of brain waves. The brain is using all these waves at any one time; however, one frequency is always predominant.

Beta:

The beta frequency is the cycle you are using under normal circumstances. Your brain waves are cycling between 14-28 cycles per second. While you are reading this book you are in beta wave.

Alpha:

The alpha frequency is the one you are using when you are in a very relaxed, meditative state of mind. Your brain waves are cycling between 7-14 cycles per second.

Theta:

A theta state is a very deep state of relaxation. The theta state is most often reached during deep meditation. It is also a sleep wave, and can be obtained under hypnosis. Your brain waves cycle between 4-7 cycles per second while in this state.

Delta

A delta state of mind is found when you are in a deep sleep. This is the state of mind that allows you to know who is calling when the phone rings. The delta state of mind cycles between 0-4 cycles per second.

We have found that during healings, with the techniques outlined in this book, we were using mostly theta waves.

Please keep in mind the analogy of things that are discussed in this book are real. They work, and they work because you are accessing a brain wave that is low enough to allow you to make contact with the creative force of the universe.

After continued practice, I found my healings became even more impressive. My results improved and my clientele increased daily, but I still encountered a few who would not heal.

One of these people who did not seem to heal correctly was a woman who had diabetes. I would work on her for a certain problem and she would complain of having pain somewhere else, and I'd work on her another time and everything seemeed to work just fine. Some areas would get better and other areas wouldn't.

Curious to find out what was going on with woman and how I might help her with her diabetes, which I believed was created by a chromosome, I went to the Creator and asked what I should do. I was shown her chromosomes just as plain as day. I was shown the defective part of the chromosome that caused diabetes.

I was then shown another chromosome, and I was told that it was part of the chromosome of youth and vitality. I was told that this particular chromosome had been changed throughout the history of the evolution of man. We had actually changed it in our own human bodies and that we no longer had that part of this chromosome.

I was excited and I was stunned. I forgot all about the defective gene for diabetes. I gave the woman with diabetes a hug; sent her home and told my friends what I had seen. I also told them that I was told to work on the chromosome and how to fix it.

That evening I was given more information and guidance. After that I was shown over and over how to change this chromosome. People came from all over when they heard about the discovery of the healing technique, and about the people we were working on and how they were getting better. More people came when they heard we were working on the chromosomes. We were working on the chromosomes all right; we were adding five pairs to each chromosonal strand in the body (they came in ten strands), activating 10 new phantom strands.

Since that time we have discovered that there are actually multiple strands and so we began the DNA Activations, activating the phantom strands in a

person's body. Understand, we are not adding strands to anyone, only accessing what is already there. Their intuition improves, their healings improve, their body detoxifies and changes, and they are able to access different planes of existence easily and readily.

At the time I was given the DNA technique, one of the persons I spoke to concerning all of this was a doctor who worked with lasers and had a good working knowledge of the DNA. He gave me the names of everything that I was seeing in the chromosomes; the shadow chromosomes, the telomeres, and everything else that I was observing. He was one of my first validations. He not only confirmed what I had seen, but his questioning of my ability to see these things allowed me to know that I was seeing something real and something I could work on

I also met another person who was a publisher. He took our new technique, transcribed it, wrote it up and published it in pamphlet form for us. These came out in 1997. But by the time the first book came out, he had changed it so much, and added so much filler, I decided to rewrite a copy for myself and for some of the other clients that I had, so that the true dictates were not lost. The copy that was rewritten became my book "Go Up and Seek God".

By the end of 1999 I had done over 20,000 readings. The techniques used for the readings, are the techniques that we are going to explain in this book. You can heal your own body using these techniques. They can be used to heal the body and all aspects of the mind, and soul.

One of the greatest things we discovered while working on our clients is that we hold the keys to our own health, our own bodies, and our own vitality. In this book I would like to share the information that I received while working on all of these special clients.   I would also like to share with you the knowledge that has been given to me by Source since my first book was published. This information will allow you to change your beliefs, and the systems that guide your decisions, in an instant. These are the beliefs and programs you have learned from childhood . These beliefs and programs have been passed on from generation to generation.

In the following pages we are going to learn how to work on four different levels. They are the core belief level, the genetic level, the history level, and the soul level. Working on these four levels the body can conquer any physical illnesses, any blockages in the body, any mental blockages--such as receiving love--thus enabling you to create the life that you want for yourself, for in reality, we are all connected to God. It is true that we create our own reality. We are going to share with you the tools to change what you formerly believed, and the negative effect these beliefs have had on you, and allow you to create the life you desire.

In this book I am going to reveal one of the most powerful techniques ever written about, so extreme caution is given to the reader. Do not use these techniques lightly and be very careful to not misuse them. The Creator has given me the fasinating knowledge you are about to receive. It has changed my life and and the lives of many others.

Throughout this book there will be examples of the changes it has made in people's lives.

Let me offer this note to the reader. The remedies, approaches, and techniques described herein are not meant to supplement, or be a substitute for, professional medical care or treatment. You should not treat a serious medical ailment without prior consultation from a qualified healthcare professional.

So even though I am going to share this information with you, we do not accept any responsibility for the changes that can occur from their use. The responsibility is yours, a responsibility you assume when you realize that you have the power to change your life as well as the lives of others.

Forward

There were certain individuals that I could not heal, so I asked the Creator why? I was given many reasons; some of which felt like "stop signs" in the creative process of healing. I would encounter these same problems over and over again, which the Creator said was genetic. Believing this was something that I could not touch or resolve, I would tell the person, "Sorry it is genetic." Finally, after I was diagnosed with what was considered to be a genetic defect, I asked the Creator how to repair this defect. The Creator answered by showing me how to fix creative defects.

The Creator told me it would take sixteen lessons. I was amazed, since the information in my first book, about the DNA and the 12 strands, took only one lesson Anxiously, I complied and waited to receive the sixteen lessons. After receiving the lesson on how to change genetics, I immediately put this information to work. My results continued to improve, but I still found people who could not be helped. I could not fix them; I could not change them at all. I would go to the Creator in the middle of a reading, or healing, and ask to know what was blocking the healing? I would hear a voice which said, "This person believes he should be sick", or "This person believes that he must be punished", or "This person believes what their doctor tells them, or, "This person really wants to die." Thinking that I had no right to change a person's beliefs, or even remotely allow myself to have such a thought, I would send the person home after telling them that they needed to work on how they felt about themselves.

Before 1999 I had used linguistic programming, hypnosis, and other techniques to change the subconscious thought patterns. Using these techniques I had been able to change a few patterns slowly, one at a time. However, they were not consistent enough for me to consider working them into my everyday healings.

Then in 1999 the Creator showed me that you could change several patterns in seconds. Some can be altered forever and the subconscious will never know the difference. I found that I was able to alter belief patterns such as "You're not smart enough," "You're not good enough," "Money is bad,"

"Money is evil," "Other's belief systems are wrong," "I can't be psychic," "I'm not a healer,"or "I'm not good enough to connect to Gods work."

I found that this would also work on other belief systems such as: "I will suffer." "I must have this disease," or "Because it is in my genes." These in addition to other patterns could be changed or altered in seconds.

Using the techniques that I had received from the Creator, I began to formulate a pattern for the techniques found in this book; patterns that I believe will change things forever.

Come with me and we will experience how powerful these techniques really are. So, let's start at the beginning.

We believe that these techniques are as old as time itself, and that they have been used for millenniums. We also believe there is an inborn knowledge in your soul that will help you link this technique to that ancient knowledge.

Chapter One

Basic Healings and Readings

The basic healing techniques and the basic reading tecniques are really quite easy to follow, however the basic reading technique is something that doesn't just come naturally--in an instant. You must practice this technique before you can see certain things, such as a heart beating. Some people find it very easy to learn this technique, others will find that they require much practice, but you can learn to do it. There is no wrong way to do this particular technique. If you follow the instructions, each individual mind will learn it at its own pace.

Before we go any further, it is important for you to realize that there are certain things that have to be done before you can orchestrate the techniques in this book. To begin with, if after reading this book you make the comment, "I am going to try this technique," you are headed for failure. You need to say instead, "I'm going to do this technique." This is based upon the principle that your subconscious does not understand the word "try." An excellent example would be found in the fact that you can not try to pick up a pencil, you either pick it up, or you don't. You can not try to do anything; you either do it, or don't do it. That is how your subconscious works.

Let's approach this with a "do" attitude. To do a healing or a reading, you start by placing the individual you wish to work on in a chair opposite yourself. Make sure that both of you are feeling comfortable. Take the individual's hands into yours, offering your hands to them palms up, allowing them to place their palms on yours. It really doesn't matter whose hands are on the bottom or whose hands are placed on top, we've just found that this was an easy way to teach the procedure.

So to continue, the practitioner's hands are on the bottom. The practitioner imagines himself or herself going up above their space about three feet. When a person imagines himself or herself leaving their space and going up above their heads, their brain waves automatically slow down to an alpha brain wave.

The reading, or healing process, in/of itself is really quite simple. It consists of 5 easy steps,*

1. Go up above yourself

2. Approaching the Creator
3. Commanding what you want
4. The affirmation –Thank you
5. It is done.

* When you are doing a healing on an individual, and you are following this process step by step, it is of the utmost importance that you draw the energy required from the forces of the universe, not from your own energy. You do so by commanding that the forces of the universe do the healing. You may also use these same forces to replenish your own energies after a healing

The reason that this is so important is because, if you do not draw from the forces of the universe, ...

* your energies will be used and you will be drained on all levels, and

* you will be psychically hooked to the client.

1. To make this process easier on yourself, you can imagine yourself as anything you like, such as a ball of light, an angel, a fairy, anything you wish to be. By imagining that you have gone up above your space to your crown chakra, your brain waves will be lowered down to Alpha without you ever having to think about it, and the moment you call upon God, your brain wave is lowered to theta.

2. Approaching the Creator. This is a very important step! There are a few basic words that you must remember. To approach the Creator you say, "Father, Mother, God, Creator, All that is." You may use any of these terms, or any other term, which addresses God. I would suggest that it might be best for you to use the term that you were taught as a child. If you were not taught to pray as a child, term it any way you consider the correct terminology for you. While some may prefer the term "Heavenly Father," others may feel more at ease using the term "Great Mother Within." Still others may prefer Source or Creator. The key here is that your subconscious identifies "there is a Creative Source." Throughout this book you will see the terms Father, Mother, God, when

we are discussing step one. Please remember, we offer these words as an example. You should place the command that best fits you.

3. When commanding the creative forces of the universe, immediately after calling upon Father, Mother, God, you are going to have to use the words "I command". This step is the major potential problem to this process. Most individuals are reluctant to command God.

If "I command," sounds too selfish from what you've been taught to say, then say, "It is commanded." I find this especially effective in healings. You need to say "I command," because that will make your subconscious have no doubts as to what it should do. And the moment you say "I command," the healing process will begin immediately. In all actuality, God is the healer; you're just witnessing the electrical connection in this universal process. "Command = Co-Creator"

Understanding the Word "Command":

SUB WORDS IN THE WORD COMMAND

CO   in Latin the meaning is "intensive" with, as in co-operate

COM   as to invite to unite or join with. As in the word come.

MAN   creator - found in other words such as:
      Manifesto - public declaration of intent or principles

      Manifold - multiply, of many kinds, a whole made up of
              diverse elements

      Mandal - a design symbolizing the universe

      Mandible - lower part of jaw which is necessary in speaking
              as we create with words

      Ma ndare - (Latin) to order

DEFINITIONS/COMMAND
    To overlook
    To have at one's disposal, as command of a language
    To deserve and receive due observance
    A signal to activate
COMPARED TO THE WORD DEMAND

De in the Latin form means

Oppose

Reverse

Remove

Reduce

4. Begin by stating "Thank you." By thanking the Creator for the reading that you are about to perform, you are telling your subconscious, "Yes, this is going to happen."

5. "It is done, it is done, it is done." Much the same as in step four of this process, by ending the command with, "It is done, it is done, it is done," you are telling your subconscious that this will be so.

You imagine yourself going over to the person's crown and entering their body through the crown chakra. Imagine going down into their brain and turning on a flashlight. As you turn on the light and look around the brain (even if you do not know what a brain looks like) if there's any section of the brain that doesn't light up, this is a problem area.

For instance, if you turn on the flashlight and the area around their eyes doesn't light up, then ask them if they are near sighted, or far sighted, or wearing contacts. If their brain doesn't light up completely, ask the person if they have headaches occasionally. Go through the body turning on a light as you go. For instance, as you go down through the neck and the neck doesn't light up completely, don't think that you are doing it all wrong; simply ask the person if they have problems with their neck.

Go through the entire body the same way. You know the silhouette of the body. You may explore the body by following that basic silhouette. As you go you can imagine what the organs look like: however, if you do not know what the organs look like, may I suggest you take the time to reference a good anatomy book.

This particular procedure of going through the body and imagining what it looks like, is easy. At first you are going to think that you are imagining it, or you're just making it up. But you will find that as you speak to the person you're working on, whatever you're picking up is absolutely correct.

The first time you go in and do a reading, you are teaching your brain how to do something it has never done before. This process is much like learning to ride a bicycle. You will not go down as deeply into theta as you will the second, third, or fourth time you do this; however, you will get results.

After you have finished going through their body, imagine lifting yourself up out of their body and rinsing yourself off with a ray of white light, a waterfall, rain, or any method that would make you feel clean and refreshed. Rinse yourself off and put yourself back into your own space. At this time, it is important for you to make what is called a psychic break.

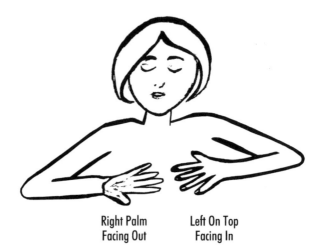

Right Palm   Left On Top
Facing Out   Facing In

To do this, you need to put your right hand and left hand palm to palm, finger touching the wrist and elbows out to the side. The back of your right hand will be facing your chest and the back of your left hand will be facing outward. Rub your palms together. Pull your right hand back to your chest and extend the left hand away from your body toward your client.

This is called a Kahuna break, and this will take care of breaking the energy that is left over. After you have finished with the break from the person, bring your right hand straight up in a knife position and move your hand up and down in front of the chest making a slicing motion down towards the solar plexus and back up again. This is called "zipping yourself up," and is used to pull your electro-magnetic field back to yourself.

It is very important that you do this after you do a reading on someone. Some examples of breaking the electro-magnetic field of a person would resemble saluting, placing a cross on your body, or any other motion that has your hands crossing this electro-magnetic field.

The second time you do a reading, you will be able to see more details. With each reading, you will become more specific. Training your mind to do a reading is exciting. It takes more than one attempt for your subconscious to "get it." Usually when people have difficulties, they are simply trying to hard, making it difficult to learn. Have faith, and do it with joy in your heart, and it will become easy.

Not only is it important that you go through the steps in the proper order, it is equally as important that you understand the steps. One of the best ways to do this is to practice.

Let's go through the steps once again.

1. First of all you go up above your space three feet. As soon as you do this your brain will enter an Alpha wave.

2. As soon as you say the words, Father, Mother, God, Creator or however you approach your Creator, your brain waves will slip instantly down into Theta. Your subconscious understands who God is, and will immediately go to the place where you feel God is.

3. The third step is to say "It is commanded." When you command God, two important functions are carried out. Number One, you are connected to God, and Number two, when you say the word "Command," your subconscious takes it as an absolute order. If you were to say, "I ask that this be granted," your subconscious will immediately go into a debate as to whether it should be granted, or not be granted. It will get lost in whether you deserve, or they deserve, and it will stop right then and there. However, if you say, "It is commanded," the whole situation is resolved, and the subconscious immediately listens.

4. As soon as you say the words, "Thank you," your subconscious accepts it as already done. Because, isn't that how you have been trained; to say "Thank you," after you have received something? The subconscious thinks it's done and immediately goes about performing what is asked of it. It is also a way of thanking the Creator for listening to us, and/or our commands; it is how you thank the Source.

5. By saying "It is done," you have notified your subconscious that it has already completed the process. This reaffirms that this action will be taking place. At this time you go into their space through the top of their crown chakra, and into their body. This time, try remembering what the skeleton system looks like. Look to see if the back is straight. If you observe that it looks misaligned, it probably is. Don't doubt yourself. Pay attention to what you imagine yourself seeing. Gently go in and imagine it happening. As you imagine it, so it is.

While in Theta, it is your imagination that you are using. This is the ability to see truth. While you are in this person's body, silently and gently looking around, you are in what is called a prophetic or healing state. As you speak and tell the person what you see, your brain waves begin to go back up to Beta. Pay attention here, any time you speak aloud, your brain waves will go back up to Beta; once you become silent again you will return to Theta.

This is teaching the mind to go from Beta to Alpha to Theta back to Alpha and back to Beta on command.

When you are finished doing your reading, always rinse yourself off. As you are doing the reading you may feel some aches and pains in your own body. Many times this is your other psychic sense picking up the client's aches and pains. This is called, "instinctual shamanism."

So, as you pull yourself up, rinse yourself off and put yourself back in your space, always make a psychic break so that you do not carry back with you the client's negative feelings, emotion, or other vibrations.

There are four different intuitive senses in the body. The first one is the empathic sense. It is located in the solar plexus. This gives you the ability to feel what other people feel. As you enter another person's space, it is not unusual to feel his/her aches and pains. One of the main reasons you need to make a psychic break after a reading is to break the empathic links.

The second psychic sense we employ is the auditory sense. Your auditory sense is located above your ears, and is the last of your psychic senses to develop. You have "felt" this before, even though you may not have known it at the time. It is the little voice inside your head that tells you danger is near. Sometimes this sense is used by your guardian angels to give you messages. Your auditory sense is what you are using when you hear a voice coming into your head during a reading that tells you this person has a broken foot.

The third psychic sense is sometimes referred to as the "third eye." This is located just above the eyes, in the middle of the forehead. The third eye is the ability to see auras. People who use this third eye are often referred to as clairvoyant. The third eye is very effective for reading a persons body, as the third eye sees in the present. On the other hand, it is not an accurate means

for predicting the future, because you usually tell a person what he/she wants to hear using this sense. In some instances while using this sense, you will find that as you go into the reading you may see different colors going through the body. It is debatable as to whether this third eye sense relies on theta waves.

The fourth and final psychic sense we will be using here is called the crown chakra. This is also referred to at times as the prophetic sense. This is the sense you are using when you experience the feeling of "knowing." You just know that it is. This chakra is the one that we will be using the most in this book. This is the chakra connected to God. This is where prophetic knowledge comes from.

Now let us take the information we've given you and go through a healing. To do a healing you follow the same procedure. You imagine yourself going up above your space, and saying, "Father, Mother, God, I command a healing on this person (silently speak the individual's name you are working on here.) Thank-you, it is done, it is done, it is done."

You now imagine yourself going into the body. If the person has a broken foot you imagine yourself going down to the broken foot. You imagine the foot mending and you see it done. As you watch it being done, so it is. When the foot is finished mending, you wrap it in a little bit of calcium. Then, you pull yourself out of the body, wash yourself off, and put yourself back in your own space.

Watching this being done is a very important part of the healing. Going up and commanding it is one thing, watching it being done is another. Only after you have witnessed the healing process is it done. There is a difference in saying it is done, and observing the process as it happens. I have many people tell me that as long as the healer intends to do it, it is done.

There is a big difference between intending to do something and doing it. I can intend to pick up my keys all day long, and I can intend to be helpful to my mate when he needs my help. It doesn't mean that I ever walked over and picked up my keys, nor does it mean that I ever did anything to help my husband. When you go into to the body, you must watch the process that you have commanded to be done until it is finished. You are there to witness it. As you witness it done, so it is done.

Although healings and readings are different, the procedures are quite similar. This technique will work unless there is a subconscious programming

saying the person should be sick. The same technique will work when a person has certain toxins in their system, and the same procedure will work when the environment has caused the sickness. It works when a person has broken a leg, and it works when a person has suffered an injury. This same technique has even been used to heal a horse's broken leg. It can even be used to fight illnesses such as cancer. Further on in the book we will discuss some other things that will help in illnesses and problems that you will encounter.

This is an extremely powerful technique. It can be used to communicate with the body. The key to this technique is that you are the witness watching what the Creator orchestrates.

If you have any questions while you are in the body, you ask the Creator. The body communicates back to you as you are doing a reading. Cell talks to cell, and every time you touch another person's body, your body automatically communicates with their body. For instance while working on a female, stop at her reproductive organs, and ask the body how many children it has "housed". The body will immediately tell you how many pregnancies it has experienced, as well as how many children are held within the heart.

When you go into another person's space you have lowered your brain waves down to theta. This allows you to hear what their body is saying. If there is a problem with someone and he/she is sick, ask the Creator to show you the cause. Always be precise in what you ask the Creator because the answer will be very specific, depending upon the question. The Creator doesn't pull any punches, and never make things more complicated than they need to be.

The other key to doing a good healing is to know exactly what you are healing. When you command something to happen in the body, it will come about. Make sure you are requesting something that is needed. If you command a healing on someone's body that doesn't know it's sick, it will never heal.

One important thing you must not to do when you do a healing, is to command the body to go back to its perfect blueprint. The body thinks it's perfect already. It has the perfect disease, it has perfect diabetes, perfect MS, everything is perfect in its universe; therefore, the subconscious will not

understand exactly what is commanded, and the person will not heal.

Once you know exactly what it is that you are going to do, alter, or change, then you have the knowledge to make a command specific enough to accomplish your goals.

This basic healing technique can be utilized on children who have hurt themselves and need immediate attention. It is wonderful to use on your family at all times. It is wonderful to take away a headache, to remove back pain, to command all pain to be gone. This healing technique will change your life. Practice it and you will become proficient in it.

There is always the question of what maladies you can heal without the person's verbal consent. If you are going to heal a bone, or a back problem or something that needs to be moved, it can be done for anyone. If you go up above your space and ask their higher self for permission to heal him/her, you will then be given the answer as to whether or not this is permitted.

Other healing techniques that have to deal with chromosomal changes, DNA, or subconscious reprogramming requires the verbal consent of the person being worked on. This must be respected. When doing this technique, always take a moment to quiet yourself, and always make certain that when you go up and command God to do whatever is needed, that you remain in their space until you are sure that it is completed.

Next, we found that the higher you go above your space, the clearer the viewing becomes. We discovered that healings can be done at three, six, and even as far as sixty-seven feet, or as high as the universe. We found that as you move yourself above your space sixty-seven feet or higher, you will hit an area of complete unconditional love. At this space it seems to change the electro magnetic pulse of the earth, wherein you go to a state of absolute unconditional love.

Several people had the idea that the more people involved in a healing, the better the outcome would be. So we gathered a group of people and together we worked on a person. We soon realized that the theta technique is so powerful that it could actually cause havoc instead of peace and relief when doing group healings incorrectly. We found that if more than one person goes

up and does a healing, everyone will be doing something different.

In one instance we had a man who came in with an injured back. We decided that we would heal him as a group. We all stood around in a circle and we all went up and worked on him separately. As we worked on this man, he lay on the table and waited quietly. When we were finished he tried to get up, and he could hardly move; in fact the pain was worse. Going up quickly I checked to see what had happened.

I could see that one healer had pulled his back in one direction and another healer had pulled his back in another direction. I asked him to please get back on the table. This took some effort, as he was not sure he wanted to receive further treatment. I then gathered the group around me, and this time I asked the Creator for instructions.

I was told to have only one person be the practitioner. The others were to stand around the table and send their love out to a certain place where the practitioner could reach out and grab their extra love and pull it down into the person.

Given exact instructions, I was told to go up above myself sixty-seven feet and have all the others standing around the table send their love up to me at sixty-seven feet. I then gathered the love that everyone was sending and pulled it in, and did the healing. Using the extra love, I pulled it into every cell of this person's body. I went in and corrected the back problem and this time the person stood up able to move comfortably, feeling no pain, and at last report he has never had to have surgery.

So profound were the effects of the group healing that we immediately tried it on a woman who was in a wheel chair and had been paralyzed for twenty years. During the class she allowed herself to be worked on. One person was the practitioner and the others sent their love up. After the class she could feel her feet, something she hadn't done for twenty years. After the second session she could feel her legs. After the last group healing she never returned. Realizing that she would lose her disability benefits if she could walk, she actually feared the thought of getting better.

This is one of the things that block people from healing and which we are going to discuss in later chapters.

Group healings are absolutely efficient. They can do phenomenal things. Appoint one person to be the practitioner, others in the group can stand around the table either holding hands or just sending their energy up. Pick a particular area where you want to go. If you don't know how far sixty-seven feet is that's ok, just command to be there.

1. Have the others send their love energy up while the practitioner goes up above himself/herself and makes the commands,
2. Father, Mother, God,
3. I command a healing on this person this day. (State specifically what must be done.)
4. Thank you
5. It is done, it is done, it is done.

Going up and gathering the love allows you to send it through every cell in the person's body. We do group healings on everyone in our groups so they can feel what it's like to have unconditional love flow through their body. We have discovered that there are some people who have no idea what unconditional love feels like. Nor do their cells. They are unable to feel the significance of this healing technique. By doing a group healing we permit them to feel unconditional love.

However most people will feel a great significance in their body. Love is the most commanding energy in the universe. True unconditional love sent through a person's body can heal many ailments, including cancer. When you are doing a healing with this technique, you are using a theta wave. The Reiki technique uses Alpha waves. While Alpha waves work excellent for pain, you will be using both Alpha and Theta.

How to do future readings.
1. Go up above your space three to sixty-seven feet.
2. Give the command Father, Mother, God, Creator
3. I command that you give me a future reading on------------------

4. Thank-you,

5. It is done, it is done, it is done.

Go out through your crown chakra, over to their crown chakra and into his/her body, then pull yourself up and hold yourself on the left side of their body (your right side), and have them ask a question that pertains to their life. You will see flashes of things that are going on in their life, present and future. You then ask the Creator to specify which is past, present, or future, and you will be shown. You will then be shown an actual account of what is going on.

The truth about readings is that a person is creating their own future. You can only tell them what they are creating at the moment. They can alter what you have seen by changing their life styles and patterns. For instance, if a person is on the verge of losing a job, he/she can always change the energy that is causing this to happen and keep their job. If you see a divorce in your client's future, advising him/her allows them the opportunity to change this from becoming a reality.

It is important for you to explain this to your clients. What you see is the path they are walking at this moment. You see the main path and this path has many smaller trails branching off from it. Any time that you give a client advice and they change their lifestyle and patterns, the original trail that you saw them walking down, may not be the trail he/she will end up taking.

A future reading is a very important, very powerful thing. You must be extremely careful not to mislead your clients into making decisions for them. You must carefully tell them that you can not make a decision for them during any kind of future reading. You can not tell them what choices to make or how to live their life. That is not your responsibility, it is theirs. You can not tell them to leave someone who is hurting them, you can only tell them what you see in their future. All decisions concerning what they are going to do about a situation must be made by them.

It is very important for the reader not to attempt to take charge of another person's life. A person's freedom of choice should never be altered or changed. If I tell a person he/she will find a quarter on the sidewalk, then they will look until they find a quarter on the sidewalk. So it is very important that

the subconscious mind not be led into something that you've worked to create for him/her.

When you go in and do a reading on a person, you are seeing what that person's life is, not what is right for you. You have no right to interject your morals, your ethics, or your opinions into a reading. The reading is for this person's alone. If you ask questions pertaining to him/her, you will get answers pertaining to this person in response.

For some people it is an definite sin to have more than one lover; for others it is an absolute part of life to have more than one person to love. You have no right to tell them what is right or wrong for them based on your moral opinions.

The practitioner has no right to put anything concerning his or her own life into the reading. What is going on in the practitioner's life should never have anything to do with the individual he/she is working on. A very false concept that has been widely spread is that people are mirrors of you. It is true that people can reflect certain things in your life and you can learn from these things. But no person is an absolute mirror of anyone else.

Each person is an individual living his or her own individual life. He/she has different feelings and has been raised with a different concept of what is right and wrong for him/her. You have no right to tell them what is right or wrong for them to do. You may offer them your opinion about what you would do if you were in their shoes, but you have no right to make a decision for the person having the reading. You are only to tell them what you see, and give them you unbiased opinion.

When doing a reading it is very important to know that your questions will be answered specifically. For instance, I had a woman who kept asking me where her next mate was coming from, and every time I did a reading on her, I kept getting over and over again that the man she was looking for would ask her for coffee three times. His father would be in a wheelchair and she would be a caregiver for the father, and that the man that she was looking for was right behind her. She waited very impatiently for this man to arrive.

This lady worked for Hospice and one of her assignments was to take care

of a man in a wheel chair. While taking care of this man she met his son. During his visits to see his father, the son asked her for coffee three times. He asked her several times for her phone number, and at last, reluctantly, she obliged. Having lost her phone number after she had given it to him, he looked her name up in the phone book. She was astonished when he called her to say, "Oh my gosh, you will never believe this, but you live right behind me. In fact, your bedroom window is facing my back yard." When I had asked where the man was, the Creator had answered "right behind her."

I had asked an exact question, and in return I had received an exact answer. At the time I received the answer it made no sense to anyone, but the answer could not have been more accurate. The more you use this technique the better you will become at wording your questions. With experience you become better and better at asking specific questions. You must remember that to make this work for you, you must keep your opinions to yourself, which is a challenge all of it's own.

I have just skimmed the surface of this subject. I have discussed briefly how to do readings and how to do healings. As you work through the healings you will see more details. You will find that as you facilitate healings, each time you will see more and more of what's going on in the body. If you are going to do medical intuitive readings, I think you would be well advised to obtain a good anatomy book. As you are shown different parts of the body, you can use this book to learn what it is that you are seeing inside the body. Before long you will know what organs you are observing.

Just wait until you see a baby kick in the fetal stage! You will get so excited you can hardly stand it.

Chapter Two

Why People Do Not Heal

I was in a bad marriage and a very unsupportive one. I felt unable to change things in my life. Several individuals told me that I had created my own cancer because of my feelings.

Something inside me told me that was incorrect. I was sure that my cancer was created by mercury poisoning. I believed this to such an extent that I did many cleanses to clear out the large amounts of mercury that I knew was in my system. The day I commanded myself to heal, my body was healed in an instant. The reason it was healed in an instant was because I believed that I didn't have to be sick, and I believed I could get better.

Working with people over the last several years I have discovered that every person is different, and every illness is an individual statement of who that person is. Whether the person has been contaminated by heavy metals, poisons, toxins, exposed to certain radiation, or whether their illness is caused by emotional problems such as anger, grief, hatred, or personal tragedies, their illness is as individual as they are. These illnesses, whether physical or emotional, should be treated in that manner; individually--one at a time.

The toxins in our world have caused many illnesses. I will discuss some of these in detail later. However, belief systems can also cause people to be sick. Hatred actually feeds cancer, and cancer grows from hatred. How and why cancer develops is totally different subject.

As a person's life unfolds, they are subjected to a vast array of feelings. As these feelings change and evolve, they have different effects on our heart, mind, body, and soul. When doing healings on people, their emotional feelings play a significant part in whether or not you can heal them. To clarify, their emotions are a large factor in whether they believe that they should be allowed to get better, or whether they should die.

Working with people, time and time again, I began to realize that the people who believed they should be sick, were sick, and this made it almost impossible to heal them and have them remain healthy. I found that people who believed they could be healed, also believed they should be healed, or that they deserved to be healed. This was true nine times out of ten.

Another group of people that you will encounter are those who just want to die. When working with this group you will come to realize that it makes no difference whether they believe in healers or not, you must respect their decisions.

Here are a couple of excellent examples of this theory.

I had a woman who came to me with thyroid cancer. Thyroid cancer is a very easy cancer to treat, if caught early. The medical profession treats thyroid cancer with excellent results. However, this woman let her cancer go uncontrolled, until at last it had spread throughout her whole system. After it had destroyed her vocal chords, she finally had the tumor removed. The tumor had grown the size of a grapefruit on her throat before she had it removed. When she came to see me, she was very sick; she was dying. Her husband, determined to save her, was trying all kinds of alternative health techniques.

Working on this lady, I decided to implement the use of light therapy. When I first began to work on her, I could see that the healings were not as effective on her as they were on other healings of the same type that I had performed. I was begging to learn which bodies responded and which ones did not. The woman explained to me that during her battle with this cancer she had found her husband stayed close to her as a companion for the first time in years. They had been spending time together, and she expressed her joy in sharing that time. It was a very enlightening situation.

After working with her a few times, she left and did not return for several weeks. Four months later, when she was critically iill, she came in again to see me. It seems that she had improved a great deal after her first visit two visits, so she decided she didn't need to see me anymore.

However, she began to get very sick again and she started to fall apart. So I went up and asked the Creator what was going on with this person, and the Creator said, "Vianna this person doesn't want to be here, this person does not want to live". During our conversation, I asked her, "Do you want to live?" She said yes, she did want to live, but she was very upset that her husband had been called back to work and was no longer spending time with her.

Once again I worked with her only to have her leave and not return. As she lay dying in the hospital her husband called me to come to see her. And he asked me to please tell him what she was thinking and saying for she was no longer able to speak. What I discovered was that she wanted to go home now and that she was finished with her life. Silently I watched this person leave this life behind and pass on into her place beyond the veil.

Another woman came to me with breast cancer. The cancer had ravaged her body to the point that her entire breast was gone. When I sat down with her and asked her if she wanted to live, she told me, "No." She told me she was tired of listening to her sister and her husband fight. She was tired of the hassle; she was tired of it all. She wanted to die!

I listened to her very carefully while she told me her story. I then went up and commanded her body to be relieved of pain. I also knew that she needed some emotional release. So I commanded the Creator to take care of this woman and help her in her plight. Three days later she died after having an emotional release from a very close friend of mine. I was unable to keep this woman from leaving, because I knew this woman wanted to die. However, after she died her husband called me and he actually thanked me for helping his wife, and allowing her to die. It was a very strange experience for me.

Another time I watched a very dear friend suffer with cancer. The doctors had informed her that it could take her life in the next two weeks. As a result of our working together, she lived for another year and four months. She was completely rid of colon cancer, and now faced an obstruction in her bowel. She went into the doctor, and believing that no matter what was done for her, she was still dying, she allowed them to remove the rest of her colon instead of just clearing out the obstruction.

I remember the day that they found all traces of her colon cancer gone, and what they had said to her. The doctor had told her he couldn't find any cancer in her colon but that didn't mean she still didn't have the cancer. After her surgery, her family refused to let anyone work on her. They told her that she was going to die, and would never go home from the hospital. She did; however, make it home from the hospital. Once home her children would not

allow anyone to work on her. They would not even allow anyone to give her vitamins. In all reality, they would not let her do anything to save herself. Eventually she passed away. Unfortunately her children had divided up everything that she had before she was ever released from the hospital. Being forced to give in to the will of others, my wonderful friend just gave up and died.

Belief systems are real, and they can be changed. For a long time I didn't believe this was possible unless you did lots of reprogramming work on yourself. I knew they could be changed with hypnosis, and I knew that they could be changed with goals, but I didn't realize that they could be changed in thirty seconds. However, they can not be changed if the person does not want this to happen.

I discovered that physical illnesses were as individual as the individuals themselves. If toxins in the body caused their illness, or other things that the body had been exposed to, the body simply needed to be cleaned up, and healed. If the illness was caused by something in their belief system, then that belief needed to be cleaned up and healed. If the illness was caused by something genetic, then that too needed to be cleaned up and healed.

I suddenly realized that many things could cause illnesses. Feelings cause illness and illness causes feelings. They go hand in hand. The first key to assisting a person, is to learn what is causing the problem, and to know this you need to go up and ask the Creator.

You are never alone when you do a healing; you are never alone when you do a reading. You are not the one who is doing the healing, God is. This is a very important fact to remember.

Again, you are not doing the healing, God is. Therefore you are not alone in the body, you can go up and ask for help any time, anywhere, under any circumstance. You need to realize that there are several reasons why some people can not be healed.

Feelings, emotions, toxins, genetic belief systems, history belief systems, soul belief systems are all involved in the healing process.

In the next chapter we are going to introduce and explain new techniques

that will change your life forever. These techinques are so efficient and so complete that we urge you to use them ethically, as God would intend. God has a tendency to deal with those people who do not follow proper ethics.

Chapter Three

Belief Systems and
How To Change Them

There are different levels of belief systems. The first level is what is called core belief. This core belief level is what a child learns from childhood to adulthood. As the child is growing up , being told consistently that he/she is smart, the child believes that he/she is smart. When you look at the child and say, "You are so dumb," then the child will grow up believing that he/she is dumb.

Many people live most of their life with the program that they can not succeed. Even if they are very successful for many years, suddenly they'll lose everything they own, or do something to defeat themselves. Not knowing why they're sabotaging themselves, they continue the process. Little do they realize that there are programs deep within them that have been there since childhood, programs that tell them they will never succeed.

I know that we do have control of our life, but it's hard to believe that you have control when the authority figures in your life make the first prints of control, by telling you what to believe and what not to believe. These are called core beliefs, things that were programmed into you, just like a computer. That's right, you work much like a computer.

These beliefs are programmed into you so deeply and so emphatically, that they are extremely hard to break. Some of these belief your ancestors have kindly handed down to you from one generation to another. You are the belief systems that were programmed into you.

So be very careful when you talk to your children because everything that you say to them is going into their little minds, like messages from a recorder. When I realized how much our programs meant to little children and how much we could effect their lives, I stopped to ponder all the things that could have been changed in so many lives, if we had just been more careful about what we said and how we said it.

The ideas and thoughts of others flow into our brains. These ideas and thoughts effect our subconscious belief systems without us ever knowing about it. I was curious to know how we could change this. So I did what I have always done, what I've done for the last several years, I went to the Creator and commanded, "OK how shall we do this." And this is what I was shown. You can use the same technique that you use for healings to change core beliefs. When you call forth the belief system, it comes forth crystal clear. To check your core beliefs, you can use muscle-testing techniques. These will only work if your body if fully hydrated.

I was not an advocate of muscle testing previously, but I can assure you that through proper facilitation of muscle testing your subconscious will answer what you believe to be right or wrong. There are three or four ways to do muscle testing. I am going to demonstrate to you how to check a person's belief systems using two of these muscle testing techniques. I will give you the instructions on four different levels and how to change the beliefs on each level. The four levels are: the subconscious, the genetic, the history level, and the soul level.

I will explain it to you thoroughly, and then I am going to walk you through changing all the different levels at once. The first step in the process is to make sure you know what you/they truly believe. What you think you believe isn't exactly what your subconscious believes. You may think that you have absolutely no blocks on money because it doesn't make any truly logical sense to your conscious mind.

That's the great thing about your conscious, it can judge quickly concerning what is right and what is wrong. This is something your subconscious doesn't do. Your subconscious is in charge of memory and feelings. The conscious decides what should be kept and what should not, to some degree, on some level. This is why all the techniques that I will be discussing with you in the following chapters have prescribed rules that are guarded and protected. Make certain that you do not break these rules.

1 Rule Number One. The person being worked on has to give you full permission to work on him/her. **YOU MUST HAVE THEIR TRUE VERBAL CONSENT.**

2. Rule Number Two. The person being worked on has to give

you verbal consent for each and every item that you work on. FOR EACH ITEM YOU WORK ON!

We're going to teach you how to pull out a belief system, discard it to God's light and replace it with a new one. You're going to learn that many of the belief systems you had as a child are still there. These systems have been added upon or added to, with new ones. So you're going to learn that you may have what is called a dual belief system. You may believe that you are rich, but you may also believe that you are poor. This is going to be very intriguing.

Again you can not work on anyone without his or her consent.

Now we are going to discuss the first of the two muscle testing techniques. You may use one of these two techniques on yourself (if you're testing youself) or on the person that you are working with. If you are the practitioner, you will ask the person to sit facing you. You will then have him/her put their thumb and either their fore finger or ring finger together and hold tightly. You're going to ask him/her to say, "I am a man" or "I am a woman." If the person is a woman and she says, "I am a woman," you then try to pull the fingers apart.

The fingers should hold very tightly.   If the fingers come apart, that is a "no" and that will indicate to you that the person is dehydrated, and you can not proceed with the testing until they are hydrated. You will then give them a glass of water, and perhaps even a tiny pinch of salt if you feel it will hydrate them faster. Salt will fool the body into thinking it is hydrated.

After the person has taken some of the water, again test the person. Have the person hold their thumb, and finger together tightly. If the person is a woman and she says, "I am a woman" her fingers should hold tightly together. Holding the thumb to the tip of the fore finger or the thumb to the tip of the ring finger, she repeats, "I am a woman". This time she holds tightly, so you know this is a "yes. Now ask her to say "I am a man," Again the finger and thumb hold tightly and that indicates to you that they are dehydrated because it should pull apart, since obviously she is not a man. Have her drink more water and then test her again. This time you see that she is holding tightly to being a woman, and she can not hold her fingers together when she says that she is a man. This would mean that she is hydrated and ready to muscle test.

Once again in review, the thumb and finger holding together tightly means a "yes,"and loosely means "no." You need to be very observant and watch how the fingers are held; tightly or loosely

Does this particular procedure work with people who are homosexual? Yes, even though they may be homosexual, their body still knows if they are a man or a woman, If you feel insecure about this, ask them if they are a puppy dog. If they say "yes," and muscle test positive, you know they are dehydrated. Again holding the fingers tightly is a "yes."

If you or your clients were raised with a particular language, the subconscious mind may have programs locked in place in that language, and the client may not test correctly because the program was locked in place using their native tongue. Direct the person being tested to speak the program aloud in their native tongue, or in the language that the program was formed in. It is also necessary, as you speak the commands with Creator, for you as the practitioner to say the commands in the same native language in order to replace programs on all four levels. Ask the client how to say the spoken program and use it as you would any other command.

Another very good way to test yourself, someone on the telephone, or clients you are working with in person, is to have them stand up and face north. Facing north, you have them say the same thing, responding with a absolutely certain "yes," or "no," answer. For example, if the person you are working with is a man, when he says,"I am a man," his body will then lean forward. If he is a man and you have him say, "I am a woman," his body will lean backwards. And vice versa. If their body does not lean at all, they are dehydrated. If they go forward on a "no" answer, you will definitely know they are dehydrated. If they go backwards on a "yes" answer, you also know they are dehydrated. So if a man says "I am a man", he should lean forward. This is an extremely effective way of learning to work on yourself.

I prefer the facing north method because it is so easy to check physically and visually.

Now, you are seated across from the person you will be working on, and

you are checking them to see if they are a man or a woman by pulling their fingers apart. Be careful that you do not cross in front of their electro-magnetic field, and change the reading. Now, we will check to see what they believe.

The first thing you want to check is whether of not they love themselves. You are going to instruct them on how to hold the thumb and finger tightly together and then you will have them say aloud, "I love myself." If the person's fingers pull apart that is a "no" and this means that he/she does not love themselves. If the person is standing up and he/she leans back on their heels that is a "no" also. .

Now, here's where the fun begins. A subconscious program can be changed instantly. Let's use love of self for an example. To begin, you have someone say, "I love myself." Lets say that their response to this when you muscle tested them was "no." You now go up above yourself and say;

1. "Father, Mother, God,"
2. I command that the program on, (insert the name here) I love myself "no" be pulled, cancelled and sent to God's light, and replaced with "I love myself."
3. Imagine yourself going down into the brain, right where the command center is, which will be right at the top of the forehead where the neurons of the brain create programs just like a computer, and you will watch those little programs and everything associated with "I do not love myself," being pulled, cancelled, and sent to God's light. And then from the right side you will see a magnificent energy burst of the neurons being pulled and replaced with the new programs.
4. Thank-you, it is done, it is done, it is done."

If you are having problems seeing this when you do the readings, or when you do the healings, move your eyes upwards towards the top of your forehead, looking upwards towards your crown and you will see things more clearly.

Core Belief Level

People spend a lifetime trying to love themselves. It is one of the things that the healers on this earth are supposed to learn, achieve, and teach to others, because no person can love another person completely until they first learn to love themselves.

The first step of the technique for subconscious re-programming is to work on the neurons of the brain.

The second thing you need to check, is to see if he/she deserves. Again, muscle test them to see if they deserve. If you receive a "yes" on this, then keep going. If you receive a "no," then go up and make the command again "Father, Mother, God, I command that the program, "I do not deserve," be pulled cancelled and replaced with "I am deserving, yes." Thank you. It is done, it is done, it is done."

Because each person is an individual, each person's programs will be different. There are several suggestions that I can offer pertaining to this. Check and see if the person is programmed to feel all alone. "I am alone," is a very deep program. Do not begin the subconscious re-programming until

you've read the remaining chapters in this book. You will then have a sufficient profile on how to put all of the programs together, because if you change one level, such as the core level, and it is kept on another level, such as the genetic level, the individual may re-create the program all over again.

So remember, just changing the subconscious will not alter or change a person. To change a person forever, you must change all four levels. The subconscious is a powerful thing. Your belief systems are powerful things. Being able to change belief systems in an instant, is an extremely powerful concept.

Genetic Programming

Now we are going to cover genetic programming. Gene replacement on genetic defects will be covered in a seperate chapter.

The genetic programming: First of all, what is a gene? A gene is a series of nucleic acids found along the DNA that make up a program for the body. Each gene has several different programs falling in the DNA strand to make sure that everything works. A gene tells your body whether it's going to be a boy or a girl. A gene is the most intricate part of the body. Your genes, located inside the nucleus of the cells, make up your DNA.

Your DNA consists of twenty-three pairs of chromosomes, a total of forty-six chromosomes. Inside each of those pairs is a mechanism and a program that runs over one hundred thousand functions for each strand of DNA. For every chromosome there is two strands of DNA. DNA itself is a very beautiful thing.

I realize that many of you who are reading this are not in the medical field, so I will explain this in terms that anyone can understand. Your DNA runs everything that happens inside your body. Over time, the cells in your body become weak and begin to die off. The DNA then takes over and gives the cells the signals that they need to re-create themselves.

The DNA was thought to be a basic structure, two very long chains that ran around each other, one going east the other going west. It has been recently discovered that the chains actually join together, and forms a circle. The chain consists of four different kinds of nucleic acids in what is called the ladder. And

the DNA itself is compiled by what is called a shipper.

Rather than explain to you scientifically the functions of every particular part of the shipper and nucleic acids, lets suffice to tell you that there are over a hundred thousand genes located in the DNA sequence and encodements of the double helix. The DNA is so long, tied up in such a tight coil in the cells, that if you were to take it out and stretch it, it would be as tall as a man.

That's pretty tight, and that's a lot of information encoded in each cell of your body. Again, there are forty-six helix chromosomes. Now here's the awesome part! Around these strands is a strange field of knowledge. This is called the morphogentic field. Science knows that it exists. It is a field of knowledge that tells the DNA to be the DNA. It's that little film of knowledge that tells a baby's cells how many legs, how many feet, and how many hands it's going to have.

Within this DNA cell, and within this construct of DNA, is genetic memory that goes back at least seven generations. Within this morphogenetic field we find our belief systems. These systems are holding on to information that has been stored by past generations for centuries. So don't let anyone fool you; you're not just physical. You're very mental and spiritual.

It was proven by a bio-chemist that there are receptors for emotions in the body. That means that there are parts of the cells that have little gateways for emotions in the body, and that different feelings and different emotions from these receptors regulate the body.

The morphogenetic field holds and stores all of our feelings and emotions. We have found that many things that we do in our lives are not just governed by how we believe, but by how our ancestors believed also. How your ancestors believed could be handed down from generation to generation, by one person's belief system into another person's.

Let's say that your mother believed it was very important to go to bed at nine o'clock because her mother taught her it was very important to go to bed at nine. However, there are some belief systems that you don't even know are there, that are definitely effecting your life, and how you believe.

One way to find out what you believe on the genetic level, is after you test

yourself on what you believe on the core belief level, or you test your client on his/her core belief level, and have made the changes you feel are necessary on that level, you can now check for the genetic beliefs. To do so, you go up above yourself and say, "Father, Mother, God, I command to see if there is a continuance on the genetic level." Then have them repeat the same thing that was repeated before, and see if the client believes it on a genetic level. Muscle test once again after this is done to ensure you have completed this task.

For instance, let's say you check someone on the core level to see if he/she believes money is evil. So the person says, "I believe money is evil". If he/she tests negative for this using the muscle testing technique, this would lead you to believe he/she doesn't believe money is evil. Now we want to check on the genetic level.

To do this, you say to yourself, "On the genetic level let's test this person again." This time he/she tests positive. This would tell you that although on the core belief level he/she felt that money was not evil, on the genetic level he/she does. And this could be blocking their progress in achieving abundance in life. To change something from a morphogentic field, you go up above yourself again, the same way you do a reading, the same way you do a healing, the same way you change a core belief, and say

1. "Father, Mother, God"
2. "I command that all genetic programs of "money is evil," be pulled, cancelled and replaced with, "money is good." Whichever program the Creator tells you needs to be replaced, take that negative program and send it to God's light.
3. "Thank you it is done, it is done, it is done," and so it is.

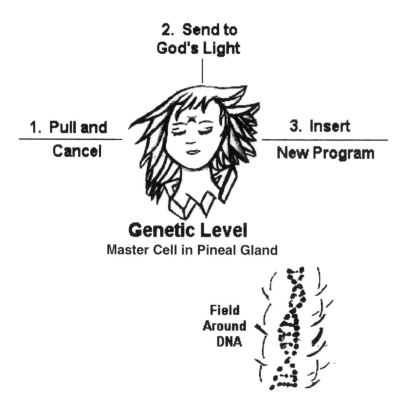

2. Send to God's Light

1. Pull and Cancel

3. Insert New Program

Genetic Level
Master Cell in Pineal Gland

Field Around DNA

For this to happen, you must go into the brain, and into what is called the master cell. Inside the brain is a gland called the pineal. It is located directly in through the top of the crown, and behind the third eye. This particular gland is called the master gland of the body. Inside of this gland is the master cell; the cell that tells the other cells of the body what to do. You go into the cell and you watch the process as the programs are pulled, cancelled and sent to God's light and replaced with positive. This is a necessary step.

You must witness the change for the change to happen. You will witness a spinning energy. This is the energy field around the DNA. As the program you have asked to be replaced is leaving the body, you will see this energy leaving to their right, or your left, as the energy is sent to God's light. Then you will watch it be replaced with a new program; that money is just money. You will see a spinning motion, and when this motion subsides, you will know you're

finished. Remember that you must observe this until the spinning motion is completed for this process to be complete.

Replacing it with the new program will alter the way that person feels about money instantly. Never, do not even consider, leaving the gene until the action is finished. When you change the morphogenetic field about how one feels, or thinks, some illnesses and diseases can heal instantly. Always watch for the genetic program's energy to be stopped before you pull yourself up and rinse yourself off.

Let me remind you that you have to have permission for every individual program to be pulled. Just because a person gives you permission to change one thing, doesn't give you a right to change anything else.

Let me give you a brief example of how changing one's feeling in the morpogenetic field can alter an illness. I knew a man who was suffering from cancer in his colon. This was his third bout with this illness. After pulling, "I hate my father," from his subconscious programming and his genetic programming, the man's cancer disappeared from his colon.

When doing this re-programming, the question I am often asked is "What do you replace it with"? You ask the Creator what should go there, and replace it with what the Creator tells you. For instance, while checking their various programs, you check to see if they have the program, "I am healthy," and by muscle testing them you find that this is not the case, and your test results show they truly believe they are not healthy. You should know that it might be necessary to take out their current program about health, and replace it with, "I am healthy" on every level.

When talking to the subconscious, the genes, or any part of the brain or mind, you must be aware that most people's minds do not understand the words: don't, don't have, I'm not, I'm not afraid. They only understand a positive affirmation. So, if you find the program, "I am afraid," do not try and fix this programming by replacing it with, "I am not afraid." Replace it with, "I am brave."

Can feelings be changed? Yes, they can. There are five different feelings that are our true feelings: anger, love, sorrow, happiness, and fear. These are

feelings that we experience every day of our lives. These feelings actually save our lives. In case of danger, fear will make us run, or, make us stand and fight, depending upon the situation. The death of a loved one or friend causes deep sorrow within us.

You have felt these emotion throughout your life. Although anger is usually thought of as a negative emotion, this same emotion is what drives a mother to protect her young. Love is the inexplicable emotion that cradles the world. When everything is going right and you are content, you feel happiness. All of these emotions, at one time or another, are necessary for your well being. The mixture of all these emotions is actually an illusion of what we believe our feelings to be at any given moment.

These emotions can also be changed or altered by the toxins and chemical reactions of the body. Toxins or chemical reactions can cause emotions such as depression. Not enough seratonin or not enough noradrenaline causes depression. Altering the DNA or the genes of the body can change these chemical reactions.

Emotions and feelings are what make us truly magnificent, and are a major part of our life experiences. All emotions, negative as well as positive, stimulate cell growth within our immune systems. It is when emotions such as anger and sorrow are allowed to go unchecked and grow out of control, that they cause a negative impact on our bodies.

The next level that we are going to work on is the third level. This is the history level. This is one of my most favorite levels. I think this is probably because I find it so extremely fasinating!

They say that memories are carried in the subconscious mind, and in the genetic, or morphogenetic field, but there are some memories that we have a difficult time identifying exactly where they originate. These are called past life memories. This level we call the history level because we are not quite sure if these are deep genetic memories, memories of people that we have watched, been in direct contact with, or if they are memories of other times and places.

Because of the highly debated issue of past lives and whether or not they truly come from past life memories, we decided to call this level the history

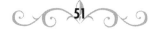

level because it definitely does exist. Group consciousness is held on this level. Many programs are the result of a "collective consciousness" due to our interconnectedness with other human thought forms. These thought forms are the result of thousands of years of human experiences, both positive and negative.

When working on this level, it is very important that you give all the time and attention to this level that you gave to the previous levels.

One of the things that is often held from a past life memory is "Oaths of poverty." Oaths of poverty are very interesting and can exist on several levels. You can change these oaths of poverty by going up the same way as when you are doing a reading and saying:

1. "Father, Mother, God I command"
2. "That all "Oaths of poverty" be pulled and sent to God's light"
3. "Thank you, it is done, it is done, it is done"
4. "And I also command that all the soul fragments be pulled, rinsed, washed, cleaned, and be replaced with the new command "It's ok to have money, or it's okay to have wealth."
5. "Thank you, it is done, it is done, it is done".

To check this level, you must command to see the history level.

At this time you will actually go to a place that is a little above the person's head, and you will actually see memories of their past lives, or mankind's past history, flash before you. This is the Etheric field around the body; this is where the work is done. It is very important when working on this level to remember what issues you are working on. When going into past life memories, you will see so many things it is easy to be overwhelmed and forget why you originally went there. That is why you must remember the issue you were seeking and make sure it is taken care of before you leave. The process is the same as before and rememember to stay there and witness the process until it's done.

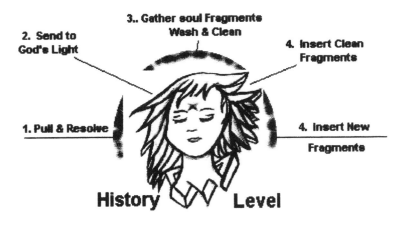

At this level, never use the word cancel; always use the word resolve. This is very important. We have actually had to work on people who have mistakenly not resolved the issues on this level, making them lose countenance and their grip on reality. Again, you say

1. "Father, Mother, God,
2. "I command this to be pulled, resolved, sent to Gods light. And also fragments of this time to be pulled, washed, and cleaned and replaced with the new program.
3. "Thank you, it is done, it is done, it is done".

If you have any questions on replacing anything, you should always ask the Creator what needs to go in its place.

Oaths of poverty are always enjoyable to work on. You will work on this the same as all the other items we have discussed before.

1. "Father, Mother, God,
2. I command that all oaths of poverty be pulled, resolved, and sent to God's light, and replaced with, "It's okay to have abundance,", or whatever God tells you.
3. Thank you, it is done, it is done, it is done."

Always resolve everything on the past life level. Always resolve it! With this resolved, you send it to God's light. And then you command that all fragments be pulled, rinsed, cleaned off and put back in where they were left off.

Soul fragments are another part of the history level that we need to discuss. There are parts of yourself that you have left in another place or time, or your family has left in another place or time. Anytime that you are in a romantic situation or any situation that will allow you the opportunity to share DNA, you will leave what is called, "soul fragments."

Anytime that you take on the sickness of another person, such as helping a child in their sickness and using your own energy to do it, you are leaving what is called soul fragments. Soul fragments are real. At this time you will command that the soul fragments be rinsed, cleaned, washed off, and put back in place with a new belief system.

The reason I picked *Oath of Poverty* as an example, is because this is where there are so many blocks to people's abundance. You will find that the *Oath of Poverty* is usually carried over in the history level. After you clean and rinse off this Oath of Poverty, pull it, resolve it, and send it to Gods light, always resolve it so the lesson is never lost. Then you pull, rinse, and clean all fragments and reinforce it with, "It's *ok to have abundance.*" Thank you it is done, it is done, it is done."

Remember, the Creator will grant you anything if you keep your ego out of the equation. You may also call for any soul fragments that do not belong in this time to be brought back and placed where they belong, which usually happens automatically, but they may have to be pushed. When you are finished, again you will say, "Thank you. It is done, it is done, it is done." Now, as you begin to work on the fourth level, the soul level, you will learn how to bring all four levels together, which enables you to work on each of them in a sequence during the same reading or healing.

This fourth level, the soul level, is a very important level.

I found that my body had a program that "*I was crying inside.*" This program did not clear on the core belief level, it did not clear on the genetic level, and it did not clear on the history level. I was told that it went all the way into the soul level.

So rather discouraged and more than a little upset, I began to wonder why it had gone all the way to soul level. I felt that once it reached my soul, it was there forever; however, I was then told, "Vianna; go up and pull your "*Crying inside*." And I replied, "I can't; it's on the soul level".

The response to me was, "Vianna, your soul is still learning. It is learning and it can be directed for what it's supposed to experience in it's existence. This is one of the reasons why you are here, to learn and experience what you create. Go up and pull your "*Crying inside*." You can do no good for anyone crying inside. If you are so busy feeling sorry for yourself or everyone else, you will have no time left to help anyone. Go up and change it."

So I went up above my space and commanded all soul programs of, "*I am crying inside*," remembered, and the remembered experience to be pulled, cancelled, and replaced with,"*I have joy*." Thank you. It is done, it is done, it is done." You can change beliefs on the soul level exactly the same way as on the other three levels previously discussed. To do this you go into the heart area of the body to facilitate this work.

1. **Go up above your space**
2. **Give the command Father, Mother, God, Creator**
3. **I command that all soul programs of _____ be pulled canceled and replaced with_____**
4. **Thank you**
5. **It is done, it is done, it is done.**

After I did this, I went up to watch what happened. In that instant I experienced a deep, peaceful feeling, down to the very depths of my heart and soul.

I felt a change coming over me and as it flowed through my body, I wanted to weep. Immediately, my nose cleared up and I could breath freely.

I repeat, the soul level is a very important level. While many feelings, thoughts and beliefs are not carried to this level, those that are can and will effect your life forever.

1. **Pull & Cancel**

2. **Send to God's Light**

3. **Inset New Knowledge & Program**

Soul Level

Is all encompassing
yet it is within

Hatred can be carried as deeply as the soul, so always check for this feeling. We are now going to learn how to work on all the four levels simultaneously. We're going to instruct you on how to put these together, how to check a person, how to work on a person, and let you begin to experience it. Note: See page 75 for a list of suggestions of different things to work on that create major changes in people's lives; things that effect money, life in general, love, etc.

As you begin to understand the four levels, you will be able to work on all four levels at the same time. Again, certain things can be changed easily on every level. Let's talk about some things that are found in the genetic belief systems.

An excellent example of a genetic belief system is the hatred that can sometimes be felt when a white person walks into certain black communities or when a black person walks into certain white neighborhoods. These feeling of resentment and hatred have gone on for centuries. Why do some people hate other people? It makes no sense at all, unless you go back and look into their genetics. However, we don't need to carry these hates anymore, this is ridiculous.

Our genetic belief systems have been both positive and negative for us. There are many books that have been written on what you believe, perhaps a few on how to change your genetic beliefs and very few on how to change past life beliefs. But to the best of my knowledge, none on how to change soul belief....until now. Why was this information given? Because it is time that we move our vibration to the level of being the highest and best that we can be.

To work on all four levels you need to start by using the muscle testing techniques that were previously described. Remember, these muscle-testing techniques will only answer you accurately if the person is hydrated with water. Making sure the person is hydrated; you may begin the muscle testing.

As you muscle test them you will find that YOU do not need the muscle testing to see what is there. As you intuitively go in, you will clearly see the things that they are pulling up and you will hear "yes" and "no." The muscle testing is primarily for the benefit of the person being worked on.

Now assume that you're going to work on a person using all four levels at once. The first thing that you do is check them for a core belief; for example, money. This is a good one to use because for centuries past it was believed that people should be humble to communicate with Deity (God) and since those who had money were not looked upon as humble, money was therefore thought to be bad.

So let's pretend that we're going to work on someone with money.

The first thing we do is muscle check him/her by having them declare whether he/she is wealthy or poor, realizing that if your subconscious believes that you are something, you are. Now Let's say this person tests out to be poor. We have him/her say, "I am poor." The person tests out yes, he/she is poor. Prior to the testing we've already gone through preparing for the testing by making certain that he/she answers a yes question, "yes," and a no question, "no." and we've made certain that he/she is hydrated and ready to

test. Now the person has tested out, "Yes, I am poor." So, we go in and we pull, "I am poor," and replace it with, "I am wealthy." Then we muscle test again, and have them say again, "I am poor." This time their hands open freely, which is a no answer. You then move up to the next level, THE GENETIC LEVEL, and the person again says, "I am poor." And once again the person checks out, "yes" he/she is poor. You then know that this belief system is definitely genetic. So you pull the belief system," I am poor," and replace it with, " I am wealthy."

As you replace it with," I am wealthy," you feel terrible conflict. So quickly you check the person and state, "Having money is bad," and he/she says, "Yes it is". So, promptly testing him/her again, you have him/her say, "I took an oath of poverty". And sure enough, this person has an oath of poverty, for he/she checks out, "yes." Immediately you go into his/her past life level and command all oaths of poverty to be pulled, resolved, and sent to god's light, and gather all soul fragments together. "Thank you, it is done, it is done, it is done."

All oaths of poverty are usually made on the genetic level, and on the past life level. However, you may need to check them on a genetic level or on a core belief level if they have ever been a priest or anything pertaining to that profession or field.

As you pull the oath of poverty, you always pull it in this manner, "Father, Mother, God, I command all oaths of poverty to be pulled, resolved, sent to God's light, and thank you for this lesson. I command that it be replaced with, "It's ok to have wealth now," Thank you. It is done, it is done, it is done." After you've pulled this, go back and check the person and see if he/she still has an oath of poverty. If they do, you need to check to see if it has gone to the soul level.

Most of the time issues are not carried to the soul level; they are usually carried only three levels deep; however, anything that is carried more than one level deep can actually get to the soul level, so always check this. The issue about money was brought up for discussion because many healers the world over think they should be humble and therefore, poor. There is no wisdom anywhere written that says humble is poor. So many humanitarian deeds can

be accomplished with money. Starving children can be fed, and hurting people throughout the world can be taken care of. However, if someone's programing is a belief that money is evil, and therefore having money is evil, this needs to be pulled so he/she does not become what they would never wish to be.

This is maximum power being handed over to you--changing a person's belief system. Another type of erroneous belief system is that you have to struggle. I believed that I had to struggle in my life, and therefore I created the first thirty years of my life as a complete struggle.

This is a program that needs to be pulled and replaced with, "Life is an adventure." Interestingly, this program is carried not only genetically, but occasionally you find it in the history level. You need to pull the program that you have to struggle to receive the good things of life. It is true, we can learn through all our experiences, but we can learn through good experiences just as as easily as we can through our bad experiences.

It is quite interesting to observe all the lessons that a healer puts himself or herself through. In so many ways I am very grateful for the lessons that I have created for myself, for this has prepared me to have empathy for people in all walks of life. However, struggles can be changed to, "Life has challenges, and, "Life is an adventure." Do not replace struggle with life is easy, or your soul gets bored and wants to leave.

Regardless, the idea that you have to suffer to learn, is false and no longer needed. We need to apply the truth that we can have goodness upon our lives; that we can experience happiness, challenge and adventure. Life was meant to be an adventure. Your souls do not contemplate whether you're having a good adventure or a bad adventure, as long as you are learning. This is a fact. So, why not make the journey a joyful experience!

There are certain things in life that you are unable to completely control. The fact remains that you can not control another person's life, but you can control your own decisions and what you create. Pulling the need to suffer will save you a great deal of time and energy. If you feel you have suffered enough already, you need pull it. Again, I am grateful for the things I have experienced.

One of the things that you will find in core beliefs is that people like to hold onto whatever they feel is comfortable. So they will struggle to hold onto programs such as, "I am alone." I watched one client struggling very diligently to hold onto the belief that she was alone. She felt that we are all born alone, and that we will all die alone; that we are islands unto ourselves. But in truth, we are constantly surrounded by unseen guardians. Surrounded by these assigned companions and the Creator's energy force, we truly are never alone. Yet we often try very hard to hold onto these belief systems.

Another belief system that we try to hold on to is the fact that we are victims. Looking back over the people who have attended my classes, I would estimate that easily eight out of ten women have been molested, and probably five out of ten men. This is not something new; this is something very real, truly unfortunate, but real. I include myself in that group of eight out of ten women. But, I am telling you that you can not let it destroy your life or give you the excuse not to live.

Pulling, *"I am a victim,"* from people is a vital one to pull. Check them to see if they feel they are a victim; if they are abused; of if they are molested. If they have any of these, pulling them will change their life forever!. Replacing, *"I am a victim,"* with the positive affirmation, *"I am a power in my own life,"* or whatever the Creator tells you to replace it with, will change their lives dramatically and permanently!

An enjoyable one to pull is the fat. This is interesting, because we have a fat gene, and here's is how it works. First of all, people have a core belief that they are fat; core beliefs are quite intriguing. People are fat for many different reasons.

One reason is that they feel they should be fat because everyone else in their family is fat.

Two, because if they are fat, they are safe and protected. Therefore, you'd better make absolutely sure you pull the program of, "I am a victim," from them.

Three, they have what is called the fat gene, which is an interesting belief system in it's own. In the generations before us, being heavy was actually a

sign of wealth and of power in many cultures. So you must check to see if they believe that fat is powerful, safe and secure.

The first thing you do is muscle test them and see if they have one of these fat beliefs. Then you command, "I am fat," be replaced with, "I am thin," or "I am healthy." And you should replace anything that has to do with "I am fat." So you go up and say, "Father, Mother, God, I command, that the core belief that "I am fat" and any remaining beliefs that "I am fat" be pulled, cancelled, and sent to God's light, and replaced with,"I am thin."

The question is, why do you cancel it in this lifetime, and not resolve it in this lifetime? This question is easily answered. If you tell the subconscious to resolve this issue, in the right now, it will resolve it for a year, or two,or maybe three years. Canceling the thought process and reinserting the new one doesn't mean that you will forget, It just means that you would no longer use that as a core belief.

Now, changing the core belief "I am fat," and replacing it with "I am thin," also needs to be done on a contradictory basis. Check and see if the person believes that he/she is thin. For every core belief that you pull, you should check the opposite. For instance, If the person believes he/she is wealthy, don't continue on from there until you check and see if he/she believes he/she is poor.

I believed I was rich and poor. Interesting concept. You can believe in two things. You have what is called a dual belief system, each one fighting the other. Some people believe they are thin and believe they're fat also. You will find that fatness is usually carried at least to the gene level. If they believe on the genetic level that they are fat, you pull, cancel, and send it to God's light, then replace it with, "I am thin." Again, checking all the other words and aspects.

We found that when telling the subconscious a person was thin and confirming it by muscle testing, it did not always mean that it had taken all the way to the genetic level. Usually though, when you check somebody, he/she will automatically flip over to what is called the genetic level and test out," no." For instance, you are re-programming someone to be thin. So you go up and

command him/her to say, "I am thin," and you command the program that "I am thin, no," to be replaced with, "I am thin, yes." You muscle test them and he/she says they are thin. Always check on the genetic level.

So, you go up and think to yourself, go to the genetic level, and have the person say it again, and sure enough, he/she still thinks they are fat. However, he/she tests, "I am thin." Going up to the genetic level you command him/her to be thin, and when he/she tests out again, they are fine. Have them test for I am fat, heavy, or overweight and replace any of these--if they come up with, "yes"--with,"I am thin and strong."

Always check on all the levels. We've found that if you stop at the genetic level you may have opened a new can of worms because of past lives levels or old genetic memories. In some tribes, especially Hawaiian tribes and some Indian tribes, the heaviest person was the most powerful person.

Therefore, they believe that to be more powerful or intuitive, they must gain weight. So make sure that you pull the program that they are more powerful or they are strong when they are heavy and that it is pulled on the past life level also. So if you find, "I am heavy" in a past life level, ask if they have any of the other above mentioned programs, remembering that heaviness was once very good, not very bad. Anyone who is of English descent will more than likely have some heaviness in his or her genetic belief systems also.

We have found that hatred is also sometimes carried to the soul level. As reluctant as we are to admit that we might actually hate anyone, this is an important issue to work on at the soul level. Pulling someone's hatred for another person has immediate effects on the physical body.

Anytime you pull anything off the morophogenetic or subconscious level you will see a physical change take place in the person. This is their belief system telling them that they are alone and unable to change their life. Changing that belief system will effect diseases immediately; people will get better immediately.

If you are doing a healing on someone and you find you can not heal him/her, go in and find out what it is that the illness is doing to serve them. And, also find out what core beliefs need to be changed. A good example of this would be the attention someone gets during an illness. When you are sick, people care about you; they send you presents, and take the time to call you and to stop by and see how you are doing.

I was working on an individual who was very weak. I found the source to be his liver. After testing this person, I decided that the problem was coming from a hatred of his mother. His hatred was so strong it was effecting the functions of his liver. So I went up and commanded that all hatred for his mother be pulled, canceled, and replaced with, "I forgive my mother." After doing this, not only did his liver begin to function normally, he was once again able to have a normal relationship with his mother.

Some people can not be re-programmed to forgive a certain person. If you encounter someone who will not take that command, it means that this person is not ready to forgive. In this case you need to command, "I release this person." So if they do not want to forgive someone, such as someone who molested them, you replace it with, "I release this person to God's light now."

Don't always force the issue of forgiveness; releasing is forgiveness in it's own way. Some individuals must release their feelings before they can be programmed to forgive. In the previous example with the individual who hated his mother, I took this belief away on his core belief. He didn't hate her on a genetic level, but he did hate her on a past life level. So we pulled it and replaced it.

This is also an excellent example of why you must test all four levels. Consequently, I went up and started working on myself. I didn't believe that I could hate anyone, ever, in the whole wide world. But sure enough, my subconscious, hanging onto the past, had a few people it didn't like. And after I pulled this dislike of several people off my body, I began to feel strength coming back into my body. As it was once explained to me, hatred consumes the energy of a person; it consumes all the energy from your body.

I was told that when you pull the people that you hate out of your body, you should replace it with a different emotion. So as I went through different people that I knew, I discovered that there are many people I held hateful feelings toward. So I began to pull these emotions off and replace them. I

was taught that it was always wrong to hate. Therefore, I didn't think I hated anybody. So be fair to yourself and muscle check. Pull anybody that you know has hurt you, check and see if you hate them. Pull the hate, cancel it, and send it to God's light and then either replace it with, "I release," or, "I forgive."

Once you pull the hatred, make sure you also pull, "I am angry with this person." The effects are absolutely astounding. As I stated earlier, when I pulled the boy's emotion of, "I hate my father," from his body, at his next cancer check, which was four days after, the results came back totally clear of cancer. All the cancer in his colon was completely gone. Cancer thrives on hatred and anger, in fact it makes it grow.

Again, we will discuss cancer in more depth under diseases.   In the meantime, changing core beliefs and changing what a person believes, and what you believe in yourself, is absolutely vital. You use the same technique to work on yourself as you do when you work on others.

You go up above yourself and say "Father, Mother, God, I command this to be pulled." You test yourself the same way you would test anyone else. An accurate way to muscle test youself is the standing facing north technique previously described. Remember to always check yourself with a for sure "yes" answer, and a for sure "no" answer, so you know for certain that you are hydrated enough for an accurate test.

Be honest with yourself on letting your body do the leaning forward or backward. This is extremely important. And by working on yourself, you will learn many things that you didn't know about yourself. Plus, it's excellent practice towards working on others. And may I remind you to thoroughly explore what you believe.

Anyone that doesn't have a negative thought or a negative process they feel they need to erase, truly must be an ascended master. And to me the definition of an ascended master means that you can probably walk through walls, and actually manifest yourself in front of anyone who wants to see it, not in a thought form, but in an actual physical form. That is the my definition of ascended masters.

In my opinion, the most important belief you can check yourself for, is to

see if you have boundaries set on yourself for healing. The first thing that we do when we work on people in class is to pull all their subconscious programs that says that they cannot do something; their fear of being the healer and doubt of being the healer. Remember that we are not the healers, God is. And depending on this powerful force can change anything.

Can you just command all negative programs to be changed in your life instantly? No, you can't command every negative program to be changed in your life instantly simply because your subconscious does not know what a negative program is or is not. This is where you use your conscious mind to make your decisions on what needs to be there.

When you're replacing someone's program, always ask the Creator what to replace it with if you are not sure. You will always get an answer; you are never alone. No, you can not command that all your negative programs be pulled from you. I repeat, your subconscious doesn't know what is negative.

As you proceed, you may think you're done, but you're not. Not until you go in and check for every belief system that you feel is blocking you.

If you have a block on abundance, then change it. If you have a block in your healing abilities, then change it. I found that I had been putting a full compartment of boundaries into my subconscious mind, boundaries on what I could do in one day for myself, boundaries on my private life so that I could actually have five minutes to rest.

I had programmed myself to set boundaries, yet these boundaries did not go into my subconscious the way I thought they did. I checked and sure enough I had boundaries on my healing ability. So I went up and I pulled all my boundaries, and commanded that all my healing abilities be boundless. Then I commanded that I had boundaries only on my personal life when I felt like I needed time. The difference was absolutely amazing. The healings worked ten times faster than they had ever worked before. I was amazed at what I had been trying to program myself for.

Listen to what you say! If you find that a woman hates men, do you not program her with the belief system to release all men, or she may leave her spouse and never be with another male. Pay attention to what you're

programming a person with, and replace programs that are proper for them. Remember, just go up and ask God what they need. This is a powerful healing process that will change your life instantly.

Always put the four levels together. Remember that if you change a program on one level, it may exist on the other three levels also. Changing the subconscious belief does not necessarily mean it has been changed on the genetic level. And if it still exists on another level it will recreate the program you have already pulled. When you're checking to see if someone loves himself or herself, make sure you check to see if they hate themselves also. Pull the, "I hate myself," and replace it with, "I love myself," or, "I forgive myself." Very important!

The responsibility of the healer is yours. You are your own healer. I was terrified to take this technique to anyone, because I was afraid of the implications that someone could do great harm to another person. Again, the Creator told me that you have to have verbal consent on every technique described in this book. So if you're pulling money issues on a person, you have to ask him/her would they like to change this issue?

The responsibility of the healer is to make certain that they watch it being done. Once the command is done, you stay there and observe from inside until it is finished. You should understand that if you imagine it being done, visualizing it is done, and feel it happening, that this is the same as observing it being done.

People often get mixed up with what is feeling, and what is seeing. If you feel a color is green, then you are visualizing it. People often mistake what is in their mind's eye or in the part of the mind they use for imagination, as feeling, and not as visualization. It is the same.

Understand that you must ask for permission before working on ANYONE. This is a law that is not to be broken. You can not change somebody simply because you wish to change them. You have to ask for their verbal consent. You have no right to work or change anyone's life; that is there own free agency. Also understand, that you as the healer not only have great responsibilities, but you must also believe in yourself. This too can be programmed into you, and

that program would be extra belief in yourself.

The fact remains that God is the healer and you are just the observer watching it happening. The person being worked on doesn't have to actually believe that you can do anything. All you have to do is go up and command God, and watch it happen. All they have to do is want to get better.

This is something you need to comprehend to fully understand this writing and this work. As far as programming goes, when your doubting your own healing abilities, pull your self-doubts. Any doubt or fear will block you from being the healer that you are. But when you pull them, not only put in that you know that God is the healer, but also put in that you live that God is the healer. Knowing and living are sometimes two different things. If you live that God is the healer, miracles will happen around you and many things will change.

Now that you have learned how to do the core belief work, we are going to show you some quick steps to make your facilitation more effective, more clear, and faster. One of the ways you can do more effective work is to do something called probing. Probing is looking for the key core belief that holds many core beliefs.

For instance, say the person wants to be rich. You can't just program a person to be rich if they believe that "money is the root of all evil." They will contradict that belief system and rebuild it. So the first thing you need to do is to ask the Creator if there is a block that is not allowing them to have or create their money. You will go up and ask the Creator which is the key base belief or key belief that is blocking this person's abundance.

Sometimes there are three or four, and at times there is only one. For instance, a person believes that "money is evil." If they believe that "money is evil" the person will not let it come into their life. Go up, pull the belief that "money is evil" and replace it with "money is just money." Always replace it with "money is just money", taking the thought of evil out of the thought form. This person will now allow themselves to have money.

One of our practitioners gave me the suggestion to visualize the belief system as a house of cards. You then ask the Creator which key belief system to pull to make the card house fall down. That is how she gets to the major base

beliefs that are holding the disfunction. If you always ask the Creator which key base beliefs are holding this belief system intact, you will get an answer. Also, it gives you the opportunity to play the "investigator," because the person you are working on will give you clues on how to work on them. I worked on a woman who believed she could not heal herself, so I went in and pulled that she could not heal herself.

As we pulled that energy, the first thing that came out of her mouth was "Well I couldn't heal myself because I didn't deserve to heal myself." I asked her why she didn't deserve to heal herself, and she said, "Because God doesn't want me to heal myself." So I checked her to see if she loved God and sure enough, she loved God. I asked her if she hated God, and sure enough she hated God. I asked her why she hated God and she said, "God punishes." Going in, I pulled the belief system that "God punishes," and put in the belief system that "God is a forgiving God, and loves you."

Immediately, the belief system, "I hate God," was gone, and the belief system that, "I cannot heal myself was gone."   All of these belief systems were cleared with pulling, "God punishes."

So when you're working on a person, you ask them why they believe something is true. First, pull the major core belief and listen to them repeat what they believe back to you. You will know when you are finished because you will feel a settling in your heart. If the person feels unsettled or the person feels any pain, then their issues are not taken care of.

When you commence to work on a person and they begin to have some neck pain, or some leg pain, work on their core beliefs until it is gone. This means that you are triggering different belief systems of which their subconscious is fighting to hold onto. This is an effective way to make everything we discussed previously come into reality much faster. You may command that all the belief systems are pulled on every level, but you must always watch each and every level.

You must witness it changing on the core belief, you must witness it changing on the genetic belief, you must witness it being resolved on a history belief, and also witness it on a soul belief. Again, some things are not held on

every level. If you don't see it occurring at that moment, then it may not be on that level, or on other levels. You must always witness the change, otherwise it doesn't clear and it will rebuild itself. You can save hours of time and be just as effective by looking for and clearing the major base beliefs that hold the other beliefs.

Core Belief Shortcut

When you are comfortable facilitating the core belief work, you can use the shortcut command to accelerate the time needed to pull, cancel and replace programs on all four levels as follows:

1. Ask permission to pull the chosen program.

2. Center yourself in your heart chakra.

3. Go up and connect to Source and make the command, "Father, Mother, God, I command to remove the programs of (name programs) from (name Individual) on all four levels at the one time.

4. Command that these programs be pulled, cancelled, and replaced on all levels, except on the History level; on this level the program must be resolved.

5. Go into the person's space and visualize all four levels coming up at one time.

6. Visualize the programs of energy being cancelled from all four levels, resolved on the history level, and sent to God's light.

7. Visualize the new programs of energy flowing in from God's light, and being placed on all four levels.

8. Stay in the person's space until you are sure the work is finished.

9. Rinse yourself off with God's light, put yourself back in your space, and make an energy break.

When in the co-creative process of connecting to God while facilitating core belief work, changing the gene structure of the body, DNA activations, the facilitator, as a natural process of the work, stops or slows time down during the period the work is being done. This is so that the incredible amount of work that is going on has time to finish without causing the client any difficulties on the physical, mental, or spiritual levels. You must realize that by

the time your mind sees it, it has already been accomplished. Remember, that you must witness the work being done and accomplished for it to truly materialize and take form in the physical world. Also, you must find the basic belief system that is the foundation of the client's problem in order prevent the client from going into a bit of a healing crisis.

Belief Systems

Negative Programs to be replaced

Positive Programs/ Suggestions to replace the Negative ones with

Cancer

Negative	Positive
1. I have cancer.	1. My body is free from cancer.
2. I hate my cancer.	2. My body is filed with love.
3. I hate myself.	3. I love myself.
4. I believe everything the doctor says.	4. I have decernment in what the doctor says.
5. Cancer kills people.	5. People live through cancer.
6. I want to die or I have a death wish.	6. I want to live or I have a life wish.
7. I will die of cancer.	7. I will live.
8. Pull hatred of those around them. (Spouse, parents, children.)	8. Forgiveness of those around them or release. (Spouse, parents, children.)
9. I have learned all this illness has to teach me. (When you're testing you get NO)	9. I have learned all this illness has to teach me.
10. I can receive and accept love easily. (When you're testing you get NO)	10. I can receive and accept love easily.
11. I can receive and accept joy easily. (When you're testing you get NO)	11. I can receive and accept joy easily.
12. It takes a long time to heal.	12. Healing is quick or fast. I am healed.
13. I am alone.	13. I am surrounded by people who love me.
14. God hates me.	14. God loves me.

Find out how this illness has served them.

**Check these programs on all levels.
Always check with GOD**

Belief Systems

Negative Programs to be replaced   Positive Programs/ Suggestions to replace the Negative ones with

Self Love

Negative	Positive
1. I love myself. (When you're testing and get NO)	1. I love myself.
2. I hate myself.	2. I love and forgive myself.
3. I am worthy. (When you're testing and get NO)	3. I am worthy.
4. I deserve. (When you're testing and get NO)	4. I deserve good things.
5. I can receive and accept love easily. (When you're testing and get NO)	5. I can receive accept love easily.
6. It's okay to be happy. (When you're testing and get NO)	6. It is okay to be happy.
7. I can receive and accept joy. (When you're testing and get NO)	7. I can receive and accept joy easily.
8. Life is a struggle.	8. Life is an adventure.
9. It's wrong to be happy.	9. I am happy.
10. I hate God.	10. I love and forgive God.
11. It is Gods fault.	11. God loves me.

Check these programs on all levels.
Always check with GOD

Belief Systems

Negative Programs to be replaced

Positive Programs/ Suggestions to replace the Negative ones with

Heavy

Negative Programs to be replaced	Positive Programs/ Suggestions
1. I am fat.	1. I am thin and healthy.
2. I am heavy.	2. I am thin and healthy.
3. I am thin. (When you're testing and get NO)	3. I am thin and healthy.
4. When I am fat I am safer.	4. I am safe thin too.
5. When I am heavy I am more powerful.	5. When I am thin I am more powerful.
6. When I am heavy I am abundant.	6. When I am thin and strong I am abundant.
7. I love exercise. (When you're testing and get NO)	7. I love exercise.
8. Every bite of food I eat is filled with love. (When you're testing and get NO)	8. Every bite of food I eat is filled with love and is good for me.
9. I care what I eat. (When you're testing and get NO)	9. I care about what I eat.
10. My body craves food always.	10. I eat only when my body needs food
11. I hate my body.	11. I love my body.
12. I love my body. (When you're testing and get NO)	12. I love my body.
13. Men/Women leave me alone when I am fat.	13. I deal easily with men and women when I am thin.
14. I hate skinny people.	14. Skinny people are nice too.
15. My body is strong. (When you're testing and get NO)	15. My body is strong.

Check these programs on all levels.
Always check with GOD

Belief Systems

Negative Programs to be replaced   Positive Programs/ Suggestions to replace the Negative ones with

Hate

Negative	Positive
1. I hate myself.	1. I love my self.
2. I hate my mother.	2. I forgive my mother.
3. I hate my father.	3. I forgive my father.
4. I hate _____.	4. I forgive _____.

If the person will not take the program "I forgive" insert the program "I release" then they will be able forgive and you will have the same result.

Forgiveness is an amazing healer.

Check these programs on all levels.
Always check with GOD

Blocking Healing Abilities

Negative	Positive
1. Healers are evil. (Ancestral fear)	1. Healers are good too.
2. Psychics are evil.	2. Psychics are good too.
3. I Fear Healings	3. I know and live healing.
4. I Doubt Healings	4. God is healer.
5. I have boundaries on healings	5. My healings work always.
6. I am blocked doing healings	6. Healings are easy.

Check these programs on all levels.
Always check with GOD

Belief Systems

Negative Programs to be replaced

Positive Programs/ Suggestions to replace the Negative ones with

Money

Negative	Positive
1. I am poor.	1. I am wealthy.
2. I am rich. (When you're testing and get NO)	2. I am rich.
3. I took am oath of poverty.	3. & 4. History or third level pull, resolve, and send to God's light with thanks for the lesson. Call back and cleanse soul fragments and replace with it is ok to have abundance.
4. I took a vow of poverty.	
5. Money corrupts.	5. Money is just money.
6. Money will corrupt me.	6. My priorities are of God.
7. I have to work for every penny I get.	7. Money comes easily.
8. Money is evil.	8. Money is just money.
9. Money is the root of all evil.	9. Money is just money.
10. The love of money is the root of all evil.	10. Money is just money.
11. The less you have the more God loves you.	11. God loves everyone.
12. People with money are mean.	12. People with money are nice too.
13. I am abundant. (When you're testing you get NO)	13. I am abundant.

Check these programs on all levels.
Always check with GOD

Belief Systems

Negative Programs to be replaced

Positive Programs/ Suggestions to replace the Negative ones with

Depression

Negative	Positive
1. I am depressed.	1. I am filed with joy.
2. I can receive joy easily. (When you're testing you get NO)	2. I can receive joy easily.
3. Depression is my excuse so that I do not have to do anything.	3. I love to do fun things.
4. I am motivated. (When you're testing you get NO)	4. I am motivated.
5. I am alone.	5. I am surrounded by people that love me.
6. I am not good enough.	6. I am good enough.
7. I am a failure.	7. I am a success.
8. I succeed. (When you're testing you get NO)	8. I succeed.
9. It is my fault.	9. I forgive myself.
10. I am a victim.	10. I am strong.
11. I am abandoned.	11. I am supported.
12. I complain.	12. I find joy.
13. It is wrong to be happy.	13. It is ok to be happy.
14. No one wants me.	14. The universe is rushing in to support me.
15. The world is better off with out me.	15. The world is a wonderful place with me. It is just waiting to support me.

Raise the serotonin when you work with gene replacement.

Check these programs on all levels.
Always check with GOD

Chapter Four

Gene Replacement

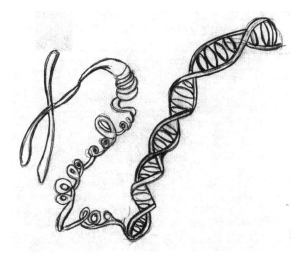

The next step we are going to discuss is called gene replacement. I was told that I had a genetic defect, so I asked the Creator how to go in and pull it and work on it. Because of this experience, the gene replacement was developed. The first lesson you must learn is that you cannot work on anyone without his or her permission. The second thing that you must learn is that inside the genes and inside the DNA, is an actual recording, not only of the defect and what is wrong, but what is going on with our memories, feelings, and particular body parts, the entire functioning process.

I was shown the DNA as it would appear in a film. I observed the film one frame at a time, and in each frame there were four different parts. One had been divided into four sections, as if it were a four square, four part, little cubicle. In that four-squared cubicle the first square was labeled feelings. The second square next to it was memories, the third square, which was below the first square, said body, and the last one, said future body. Please note the four parts of the gene that we are dealing with:

1. FEELINGS
2. MEMORIES
3. BODY
4. FUTURE BODY

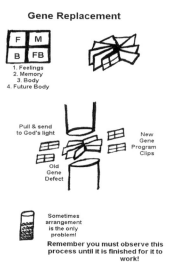

Gene Replacement

F	M
B	FB

1. Feelings
2. Memory
3. Body
4. Future Body

Pull & send to God's light

New Gene Program Clips

Old Gene Defect

Sometimes arrangement is the only problem!

Remember you must observe this process until it is finished for it to work!

After observing the clip I was reminded that we not only keep our memories of what has happened to us, but we keep the feelings associated with those memories also. For instance, let's say a person is nearsighted, and the nearsightedness is genetic. This nearsightnedness might be caused because the child doesn't wish to see what is going on in the world around them because things are too tragic, too traumatic. Farsightedness is often caused when a child does not wish to see the things happening in the future.

We discovered it wasn't the child's vision of the world, this not wanting to see what was going on, as much it was the grandmothers sadness from years and years before and of the grandmother's not wanting to see what was going on because of her overwhelming emotions, thus leaving a defect or a weakness in that gene. Pretty interesting, huh?

So I was told to pull out that clip and replace it with a new one. I was also shown that these clips aren't actually clips, but formations of a circular nature. These formations look almost like a Rolodex. Each clip was connected to other clips likened to it.

And the way that I was shown to work on it was to call it forth, "Father, Mother, God, I command that the gene for nearsightedness be pulled, or the defect for nearsightedness be pulled, canceled and replaced." And as it would be pulled, I would see the four sections being pulled. Then I would replace the four sections with the perfect program for eyes with 20/20 vision.

The first thing you would work on in this clip is the feeling. For instance, the feeling of not wanting to see would be replaced with the feeling of truth. In replacing the feeling, I would actually feel the emotion as it was replaced into the DNA.

The second part of the clip you must work on is the memory. The memory would be replaced with memory of seeing truth.

The third part of the clip we shall work on is the body. And the body would be replaced with the perfect eyesight. To replace this part of the clip you must facilitate the light to hit the back of the eye in the exact spot for perfect seeing, making correct contact, thus making acceptable healing for the eyes.

And the fourth and final square was what is called the future body. This I

would also replace with the perfect sight. It is important to work on the future body because the body and its parts can recreate old programs.

Have you ever wondered why some people that you work on get sick again later on? Sometimes it isn't just a subconscious program blocking their healing and allowing them re-create it, you also have to remember that we are constantly re-creating ourselves, and that the future body needs to be healed also.

When facilitating gene replacement you replace it with the perfect clip of the four square pattern. As you do this you can watch the clip begin to spin in circles, because it is really part of what is considered a cylinder. If this process happens so fast you cannot observe it, and you would like to see this in more detail, then you can call for a reply and ask to see the process being performed at a speed you can observe.

Remember that the work is not finished until you have observed it completed. You should also be aware that defects come in pairs. The other defect may be something altogether different. Once again, do not be afraid to ask God for assistance in finding the other defect.

When working with gene replacement, you should be aware that the results could sometimes take a little time. The new codes will not be in effect until the new cells have replaced the old ones.

As all the pieces are pulled out and replaced with the new program, the person's eyes will suddenly become corrected. While observing this process, or any other process, if you find it difficult to focus on it, move yourself closer or farther back to remedy this.

If you do not see the clip pull out, then it simply can be changed by rotating the genetic structure. Watching the clips pull out until it is finished is your controlling part and always replacing what is best for the person by asking the Creator what needs to go there. As one clip pulls out, you will watch several follow. One genetic defect means that there are several changes on many genetic strands, not just the one.

Always stay in and watch until it is completed. The whole genetic structure must be changed completely before you pull up and rinse yourself off and put yourself back into your space.

Any time you're working on the genetic level you need to go up, call upon God, and go into the pineal gland, into the master cell. This is where most of the work is completed. Always command the change to come forth. If you watch the clips come out, always replace them with the right and proper feeling, memory, and body. If you do not know what the eye looks like and you are afraid that this will effect your ability to fix the eye, remember, all you have to do is to call forth and command perfect vision for a person of a certain age, and the Creator will do the rest. Be specific.

You can work on nearsightedness in two ways. You can go right into the eye, change the curvature of the eye itself, and correct the person's nearsightedness. And you can also correct it from a genetic pattern. Either way works. Correcting the eyes with a genetic pattern will hold steady and strong. If their eyes are genetically nearsighted, if it is being passed down from generation to generation, they will re-pattern themselves back again after you've corrected it on the outside.

This means that a person's eyesight will improve until their genetic structure and knowledge catches up to them. Although I do not have an exact time frame, it should take only about three months to catch up to them. This being about the length of time it takes for the cells to divide.

Changing them on a genetic factor means they can not revert back to their original program. Eyes have improved several degrees, eyesight has been clearly more visible, and perfect sight has been granted by using these techniques.

Also understand that the eyes are the windows to the soul. As you change the gene, and the pattern of the memories, the person's feelings and memories will come up and come forth to be released.

Learn about the eyes, learn about the genes, learn about diseases, and concentrate on what you need to learn to be more specific in what you're commanding. Being specific about commanding good eyesight is all that's needed. I have watched peoples entire retinas sew themselves back up from degeneration by simply commanding the eye to see perfectly, and watching

their retinas be sewn. So perfect was one woman's retina, that the doctor she went to see a week later asked her who had done her eye surgery. He stated that he had never seen such fine work in sewing up the retina so precisely.

Sometimes there are so many feelings, and so much sorrow hidden in the past, that the person is limited to how much they can release at one time. But by helping the eyes improve by only one or two degrees at a time, eventually they will improve completely.

Let's further explain the genetic patterning of certain disease and defects. Take a defect for instances, that just happens because one amino acid is in the wrong place. It really wasn't grandma's fault, it really wasn't grandpa's fault, and it wasn't some kind of drug altering effect from a drug taken by the mother.

In cases such as this, the Creator will take you in, and show you that part of the clip in the master cell that is not correct. All you have to do is command the part that isn't correct be replaced with a new clean replacement. If you are not certain what to replace it with, ask God. I use what is called the copycat method.

For instance, a client came to me who was unable to produce red blood cells. After going in for several transfusions, she called me for help. I did not know exactly how many red blood cells I needed to command the body to make. At the time this occurred, my little granddaughter was in the office visiting, so I used my granddaughter as a pattern to see what the correct amount of red blood cells should be in the human body. I reached over and touched my granddaughter's shoulder. This gave me a pattern that I could use to replicate for this woman's body. I then went in and commanded that the red blood cells begin to replinish themselves on the DNA level, and commanded that the genetic part of her genes would match my healthy granddaughter's genes. The outcome was successful. The woman began to produce more of her own red blood cells. Things like this can be done easily by making the command precise in what needs to be done.

Next is depression. There is such a thing as genetic depression. This is something that has been handed down from grandmother and grandfather, to mother and father, and so on and so forth. This is genetic. It is a genetic defect

where the body does not produce enough seratonin.

To the best of my knowledge the medical profession has discovered that there are sixteen different forms of seratonin in the body, and they're still finding more. Seratonin is a powerful brain chemical that is released to balance a person's moods. Seratonin produces feelings of joy, happiness, calmness, and the ability to handle and solve stressful problems.

The opposite of Seratonin is the powerful brain chemical Noradrenelin. This particular chemical is released in cases of flight or fight. In some cases noradrenelin is higher than it needs to be, and seratonin lower than it should be, creating a particular characteristic of a manic depressant. People with low seratonin rates are depressed. They have no idea why they're depressed, they're just depressed.

To alter the seratonin level on a genetic level, you must go into the person's genetic level and command that all seratonin levels be raised and changed. And you need to envision the scale being raised up to the seratonin level of a normal individual between the ages of twenty-four to twenty-eight years of age and in healthy condition.

As you raise the seratonin level you will actually watch it change on the genetic scale.

Regulating seratonin is very interesting, since there are so many different kinds of seratonin. And often the body will readjust to the new seratonin level and then later will need to be altered one more time. Altering someone's seratonin level is a wonderful experience, but you must also change it on a subconscious level.

Some people have depression programmed into their being, and it literally will create depression again, simply because of a core belief. You need to go into the core belief and pull out ,"I am depressed," and replace it with, "I have joy."

You also must check it on the third level, which is the history level, and sometimes even on the fourth level. Clearing all levels will actually change depression instantly.

We have numerous cases, too many to even count, of people who have

been changed completely and no longer need their medications. However, you are not a doctor, you can not take a person off their medications; only their doctor can so this. You must be certain that any changes done with the seratonin or noradrenelin levels, has taken effect, and that you feel they are healthy before any transitions, such as the removal of medications, may take place.

The effects of changing depression are absolutely phenomenal. Again, you must change their core beliefs that they are depressed, or they will re-create it.

Another item that often causes depression, yet which is very often overlooked, is mercury poisoning. If the person has a mouth full of fillings and these fillings are amalgam, they may not have genetic depression, they may be depressed simply because of mercury poisoning, So you also need to look into this.

When changing the genetic structure of the body by going up and asking the Creator what needs to be done, sometimes you will only be directed to alter or replace part of the genetic structure.

Many diseases are caused simply because one particular amino acid is in the wrong place. Such diseases as these will actually move around and change their placement in the genetic structure when you command it to be changed. For every one defect there is usually one defect connected to it. Find the second one and the work will stay.

Psychic healings are real. Do not be fooled by skeptics. Psychic healing is probably the wrong wording. Heavenly healings are real, and they happen every day.

If you've mastered this so far, you are going to soon realize that you can actually go up, call upon God, and go into Theta. You are also going to realize that you can actually go into the body and command it to be healed.

And you will soon realize that you can change the way you believe, the way you think, and the way you feel.

Many genetic defects can be changed just by the way you think and feel. By changing core beliefs, you can change enormous amounts of genetic

defects. However, just as a reminder, different poisons and toxins found in the body can also cause genetic defects.

Once the programs are removed, it is the responsibility of the client not to recreate new negative programs by repeating negative thoughts, and saying negative things about themselves. It takes many positive affirmations to create a new belief. So, be kind to your body, and use the tools we are giving you to create new positive programs.

Chapter Five

Poisons & Toxins

In this chapter we're going to discuss some of the environmental poisons that are hindering us today in our world. Toxin's are an interesting subject, for it is said if you are a truly "enlightened being" toxins will have no influence on you. However, most of us are not yet ascended masters. Most of us have not moved our vibrational level up high enough to have attained this status, so there are some things that you need to be aware of. The first thing we're going to talk about is environmental toxins, starting with Mercury.

Mercury poisoning is real. Mercury causes certain ailments in the human body, one of which is cancer. Mercury poisoning is more common than you think. Mercury is found in a large variety of substances. One of the substances that contain mercury called amalgam.

Amalgam is the substance quite often used by dentist in fillings. These fillings have large amounts of mercury in them, and despite what you've been told, the mercury leaks from these fillings.

Mercury poisoning can cause depression, cold extremities of the hands and feet, and suicides. Mercury poisoning causes tumors, and numerous other ailments, including diarrhea, shakes, and bloated abdomens.

Mercury poisoning is fairly hard to clean up because mercury attaches itself to the cells. In fact mercury is so common that it was found in a series of flu shots. Even though the medical profession are mindful that mercury is poisonous to man, at one time flu shots did contain mercury.

Mercury poisoning is so common that people die every day from it. More than one doctor has noted the link between mercury and Alzheimer and Parkinson's disease. One of the very few things that will pull mercury out of the body is something called Coriander.

However, the Creator has said that if we change one atom in the molecule of mercury, we can change it to a harmless substance. But, until you get to the point where you feel you're performing at that level of perfection, I would suggest that you use Coriander to pull it out of your body. Selenium and liver cleanses will also help to clean mercury out of the system.

To take care of mercury poison in your own body, I suggest that the first thing you need to do is get your amalgam fillings out of your mouth. Second,

make sure you find a good dentist to do it. Very few dentists are trained to remove mercury correctly and safely; however, there are some enlightened dentists in every state. Make sure you find one who knows how to handle mercury before you let anyone touch your teeth, because mercury has to be pulled in a certain way.

After releasing the mercury from your system, you will find that you are no longer temperamental and no longer experience such mood changes. When you're working with someone, and they have questions or complaints about depression, check and make sure that they do not have amalgam fillings. Amalgam and mercury poison is quite common, at least twenty percent of the clients I speak to have mercury poisoning. There is probably a higher percentage than that, but at least that many find it effecting their daily lives.

Another dangerous toxin that is found in human bodies is one called Acetaldehyde. Acetaldehyde is a by product of yeast. If the person has had candida, they definitely have acetaldeyhde in their body. If the person has been on antibiotics they will have acetaldehyde.

This by-product doesn't ever go anywhere. It stays in the body and stays in the cells. It stays in the tissue and causes allergies, it makes the body ache all over, and can cause loss of memory. Anyone suffering from acetaldehyde can take a mineral called Molybdenum. Molybdenum will go in, change the acetalehyde to a substance the body can flush out of its system; otherwise, the body is unable to break it down. Molybdenum is an element, it is a trace mineral, very much like zinc and other trace minerals.

Molybdenum used to be found in all our fresh fruits and vegetables but due to some modern day farming practices it is no longer found in most farm products. Molybdenum should be taken in a dose of one hundred micro grams a day to start and increased to three hundred micro grams for at least four months.

Start with the 100 micro-grams a day and slowly increase the amount until you have reached the 300 micro-grams a day limit. It is suggested that doses as high as 500 to 1000 micro grams can be taken; however, I suggest that you not take more than 500 just as a precaution. After four months you will begin to feel completely different.   Actually, after one week you will notice a difference. Your mind will be more clear and your thoughts will be better. It is also noted that molybdenum will make the body ache if taken in large quantities and if you have large amounts of acetaldehyde in your body.

Be cautious in taking molybdenum, making certain that you take small doses at first, since the healing crisis initiated by the molybdenum may cause you discomfort and inconvenience. Realizing that taking molybdenum could cause the body to ache, you must remember that by allowing it to draw the acetaldehyde out of your system you will feel like an eighteen-year-old again. By pulling the acetaldehyde out of your system, you will also find out that you will begin to remember things phenomenally well.

Other toxic poisons such as lead, copper, and other trace minerals such as aluminum, can be found in many of your household appliances and foods that you come in contact with every day.

Other environmental poisons such as e-coli are causing massive problems. We are now finding e-coli and other micro-organisms invading both our public and private water systems. There is now very few truly pure waters on the earth. We now must buy our water, fulfilling something that has been prophesized for ages.

There are other environmental poisons: carbon monoxide poisoning from cars, traffic, pollution, and all of these have harmful environmental pulls on the body. We caution you to do the best you can to keep your body healthy and strong. We advise you to pull all the mercury and all the acetaldehyde out of your body.

We admonish you to eat good wholesome foods. Since most of our fruits and vegetables do not have adequate vitamins and minerals anymore, we advise you to find a good source of vitamin and mineral supplements.

Another group of environmental poisons that we must deal with now are pesticides. Zinc and calcium will pull many toxins associated with pesticides. One form of widely used pesticides is DDT. To pull these pesticides from your body you should use blue and green algae. One of the most dangerous substances to pull out of the body is something called asbestos. Once it gets

to the lungs it opens up like a wiry kind of barb wire and hooks in. The only thing that will actually pull asbestos out, are the herbs spirulina and chorella, both of which will attach to the asbestos and pull it out.

Do a precautionary check on your body. See what you have been exposed to. Our bodies were made to live for two hundred years. I'm going to tell you how to use genetic programming to actually change you to be able to live much longer than society anticipates. We'll tell you how to pull all genetic programs for getting older. Use this with caution; it can make you ill for a few days as your body tries to detoxify all the toxins that might be residing in your system.

You should go up above your space, about sixty-seven feet, and make the command, "Father, Mother, God, I command that all genetic programming for getting older be pulled, cancelled, and replaced with youthfulness, vitality, and forever young, my cells regenerating. I command this, so be it. Thank you. It is done, it is done, it is done, and so it is." Then you need to go into the pineal gland and watch this transition occur. You will watch what looks like millions of telomeres pulling out from every DNA strand. Do not leave until this is finished, and replaced with shiny new ones.

METAL TOXICITIES

Metal	Effects	Items That Contain Them	Treatment

Aluminum Poisoning	Alzheimer's Disease
	Dementia
	Senility
	Tumors
	Kidney Problems
		Anti-acids, Cake Mixes
		Baking Powder, Frozen Dough
		Tooth Paste, Rising Flour
		Antiperspirants, Pickling Salts
		Cans, Anti-Diarrhea Products
		Foil, Buffered Aspirin
		Drinking Water (Some drinking
		    water manufacturers add it to
		    keep cloudiness out of the
		    water)
			Pumpkin Seeds
			Cayenne Pepper
			Red Cabbage

Arsenic Poisoning	Metallic Taste	Household (Pesticides, Insecticides, and Herbicides) Mirrors	Selenium Vitamin C
Cadmium	Cancer Cardio Vascular Diseases	Coffee Tobacco White Bread Batteries Paints	Zinc Calcium Amino Acid
Lead	Lack of Will Power Tooth Decay Allergic Reactions Bone Problems Nervous Disorders MS, High Blood Pres. Tumors Hyperactivity Fatigue, Irritability Neurological Funtions	Paint, Porcelain Enamel Water Pipes Tin Cans, Rubber Exhaust, Varnish Tobacco Smoke Some Hair Dyes Certain Plastics Flint Glass Evaporated Milk Fungicides	Basil Rosemary Red Cabbage Chamomile Tea Vitamin C Vitamin E
Mercury	Tumors Leukemia Suicidal Tendencies Loss of Hearing Loss of Memory Parkinson's Disease Alzheimer's Disease Anxiety Depression	Amalgum Some Flu Shots Paints	Liver Cleanse Chorella Celora Selenium Vitamin C Coriander

Chapter Six

Vitamins & Minerals

This is a brief chapter on the uses of vitamins and minerals

Vitamin A is required for reproduction, maintenance, and for tissues. It is beneficial for the treatment of acne, psoriasis, skin disorders, and for use with chronic ulcers. It helps the immune system; it's also used in the treatment of cancer. Vitamin A is used for the absorption of beta-carotene and it is beneficial for the lungs.

Deficiencies of vitamin A show up in the skin, the glands, the mucus membranes, and in the form of gastritis. Vitamin A is safe to use on clients who have frequent sore throat, cold sores, flues, bronchitis, and respiratory infections. Most all fish products are high in vitamin A, such as fish oil, halibut, and salmon. It is also found in beef, chicken liver, and eggs.

Toxicity in vitamin A occurs any time that you use over 100 thousand IU's of active vitamin A daily over a long period of time. It is deemed safe to use 80,000 to 100,000 IU's for a short period, except in infants, where 15,000 IU's, will cause major problems.

Vitamin D is actually made by the sun. It is important to have sufficient amounts of vitamin D so you can metabolize the calcium and phosphorus in your body. Children with rickets have deficiencies of vitamin D. Symptoms of Vitamin D deficiencies in children are stunted growth, tooth decay, weakness, and irreversible bone deformities. In adults, vitamin D deficiencies can cause difficulty in labor when having children. Hypoglycemia is associated with low calcium in the blood, as is osteoporosis. These can be directly related to vitamin D deficiency because you have to have vitamin D to break down your calcium. A thousand units per day of Vitamin D appears to be safe. However, overdosing on vitamin D is irreversible. Too much vitamin D can make you sick to your stomach, along with other symptoms such as loss of appetite, headache, diarrhea, fatigue, restlessness, or worse. I suggest use four hundred to six hundred IU's a day for vitamin D. Vitamin D is also found in many supplements such as calcium.

Vitamin E. This particular vitamin is directly related to aging. Taking the

daily requirement of Vitamin E may help slow the process of aging in us. It is absolutely phenomenal when working on cancer. Vitamin E has amazing powers to increase your muscular regeneration. It helps the cells in your lungs, your liver, your heart, and your blood. Vitamin E has unbelievable powers for helping your sex life. Tests have shown that it is definitely a sex vitamin. It is a very important supplement for the blood, helping platelets to stick together. It is efficient in healing wounds. It is absolutely vital in minimizing scar tissue. As I stated before, it is absolutely phenomenal in the treatment of cancer. The vitamin actually consists of four substances, called alpha, beta, delta, and gamma.

Another name for vitamin E is tocopherol. This is a vital component in cancer prevention.

It is wonderful for cardio vascular disease prevention, core circulation, aging, premenstrual syndrome, prevention of excessive bleeding, and premenopausal hot flashes. The daily allowance is between two hundred and eight hundred units. If you have high blood pressure you should not take large amounts of vitamin E, unless you're being monitored by a medical professional. Toxicity effects occur when you take over twelve thousand units a day.

Vitamin K is found in food and the bacteria in our intestines also create it. Vitamin K is an important function in helping blood to clot when we are wounded. Toxicity effects appear at levels over 140 micrograms per day. You will find that red blood cells die more quickly than usual if they have too much vitamin K. Good sources of Vitamin K are spinach, green cabbage, tomatoes, liver, and lean meat. Other sources are whole wheat, strawberries, and egg yokes.

Next we will talk about vitamin B. Vitamin B should always be taken in a B complex. By taking vitamin B in a complex, your body can break it down much easier. Vitamin B is used to produce energy.

Vitamin B1 is also called thiamin; it has to do with the metabolism of carbohydrates in the body. It is effective in helping with conditions such as anxiety, it helps when you are on a diet, and it is also used for emotional and physical stress. Optimal daily allowance is twenty-five to three hundred Mg's, for men and women. A classic kind of deficiency from vitamin B1 is Berri Berri.

It has also been determined that people who are schizophrenic actually are very low in thiamin.

Vitamin B2 is called riboflavin. It is used as a protein metabolism for the enzymes. It is necessary to transport oxygen to cells. It's used for tissue repair during physical stress. Major medical problems such as burns, injuries, surgeries, tuberculoses, and fevers cause a higher demand for vitamin B in your body. People that have anemia also have a shortage of B2. Vitamin B2 promotes healthy eyes, it is found in the pigment of the retina. Some of the diseases treated with this particular Vitamin B, although you should always use it in a B complex in my opinion, are stress, cataract prevention, carpal tunnel syndrome, depression and anxiety.

Vitamin B3, known as niacin, is one of the very few things that will pull out radiation. In several studies it appears that niacin is effective against more than one type of carcinogen. It is associated with the prevention of many types of cancer.

Deficiencies of niacin are a major factor in the development of some diseases, circulation problems, high cholesterol, anxiety and depression. Examples of excellent food sources for niacin are wheat, fish, milk, cheese, whole wheat, potatoes, corn, eggs, broccoli, tomatoes, and carrots. However, it is often presented in food in a form that is not always absorbable. Lots of B3 can be lost when cooking vegetables. Steaming your vegetables will help with the loss of niacin when cooking.

Vitamin B6 is also known as pyridoxine. Pyridoxine is one of the most essential, widely utilized vitamins in the body. It is a co-enzyme that is used in over sixty enzymatic reactions involved in the metabolism of the amino acids, the essential fatty acids. Therefore, it is needed for proper growth and maintenance of body functions.

Deficiencies in pyridoxine brings forth an astonishing variety of symptoms and all of them usually effect the nervous system or changes in the skin. The nervous system is dependent on B6 in a variety of ways. Problems typical when we are deficient in our amounts of pyridoxine are depression, confusion, dizziness, insomnia, irritability, nervousness, the feeling of needles being

pushed into the feet and hands, and even the brain's functions. Food sources for pyridoxine are carrots, eggs, spinach, peas, meat, chicken, and fish. Many people who have MS have done quite well while being treated with B6. PMS, premenstrual syndrome, is often eliminated with the treatment of B6. B6 helps with kidney stones, and it can also be used as a diuretic. Carpal tunnel syndrome is usually caused by the lack of B6. Asthma can also be treated by using B6.

Vitamin B12 is also called cobalamin. Deficiencies from lack of vitamin B12 show up as anemia and fatigue. Most alcoholics are short on B12. Of course alcoholics are also short on seratonin. People with gastrula problems are often suggested to use B12, and B12 can also be given to women who are pregnant and having problems with morning sickness. Chief food sources are beef kidneys, lamb, beef, and veal.

Other good sources are mackerel, herring, cheese, clams, sardines, salmon, crab, and oysters. Optimum daily allowances are from 200 to 300 mcg. for men and women. There are no known toxicity defects from taking too much of this vitamin.

Next, let's discuss a vitamin called folic acid. Folic acid is closely related to vitamin B12 in the body. It is involved with the metabolism of amino acids. B12 is needed in the reproduction of RNA and DNA. It is vital for the cells themselves. Many aspects of the immune system are effected by deficiencies of folic acid. Depression, anxiety, and anemia can be treated by folic acid. It is suggested to take folic acid with molybdenum.

There are no known toxicity defects attributed to folic acid; however, women who are taking folic acid supplements, especially if they're currently using contraceptives are at risk.

Pantothenic acid converts into a co-enzyme, which is used during the metabolism of fats. Pantothetic acid is used for joint inflammation, depression, anxiety, and arthritis. There is no known toxicity effects from panathetic acid. It has been known to specifically help those with rheumatoid arthritis and stuffy noses.

Of all the deficiencies I have felt, few have shown up more than those

having a deficiency in calcium. I believe that mineral deficiency is causing many of the illnesses that are on the earth at this time. Calcium is needed to help heal and maintain our bones. It builds and maintains the bones while at the same time it gives vitality and endurance to the body. It helps maintain mental stability. It helps keep your muscles fit. Calcium must be used with vitamin D and magnesium.

Magnesium is necessary to relax your nerves. It relieves what is called brain lag. It's also used to keep your intestines functioning, so it's beneficial as a laxative. It is used as a motor stimulant to the brain. As I mentioned, calcium, along with magnesium deficiencies, are the highest deficiencies I've ever found. There are very few people that I have looked at that actually have enough calcium in their bodies.

People who have healing abilities seem to be low on calcium. It appears that lots of calcium is consumed in effecting connections of an electrical nature; therefore, I tell people who are going to do any kind of healing work to insure they take plenty of calcium. And by that I mean a live calcium, which requires a chelated calcium. Calcium seems to be the one mineral that is definitely used up when you work on other people.

It you don't have enough calcium, you will have what is called osteoporosis. Osteoporosis has been studied for several years and they have finally concluded that the cure for osteoporosis is calcium. High blood pressure can also be associated with the lack of calcium. Although the levels have always been debated, you can take anywhere from 1000 to 2500 micrograms daily. Dead calcium, or forms of calcium that can not be absorbed by the body, become a toxin in our system. Dysfunctions of the kidney are associated with lack of the correct form of calcium.

An interesting fact is that we actually absorb as little as twenty to forty percent of the calcium from our food. We have found that milk products do not carry as much calcium as they used to because all milk is now pasteurized and homogenized. A really good source of calcium is carrots because it is live calcium. Live calcium breaks down dead calcium deposits.

Due to the depletion of our soils, minerals are no longer made as available

to us as they once were. A suggestion for you, if you are taking minerals, is to take a chelated mineral. It is easier for chelated minerals to get into the blood stream because the intestinal wall is very thin and the cell wall is actually smaller than minerals which are not chelated.

Thus absorption of non-chelated minerals is difficult. It is also important to note that when eating a high fiber breakfast and then taking your vitamins, that the fiber is digested first and the vitamins are often thrown out. So if fiber is a part of your everyday diet, take your vitamins at least two hours after eating it. Finding a chelated vitamin or mineral is extremely important. Low magnesium is associated with angina, heart problems, and high blood pressure.

Zinc is a phenomenal mineral that is used in pulling heavy metal toxins out of the body. Zinc should be taken in a chelated form. Daily suggested use of it is 30 to 50 milligrams. Toxicity occurs at 2000 milligrams. A lack of zinc in your system will cause you to have poor night vision. Without zinc your immune system will not function up to it's capabilities and you will find you are a prime canidate for prostritis.

Without the proper amounts of zinc you will find a decrease in your sense of smell and taste. I want to state once again that zinc is phenomenal at pulling out heavy metals such as lead. As zinc will also pull copper out of the body, you need to be sure that when you are taking a zinc supplement, you take one that has copper in it.

A common mineral our bodies need is iron. Iron is needed for the red blood cells in our body. Approximately seventy-five percent of the hemoglobin in our red blood cells is responsible for carrying the oxygen through our lungs. Major deficiencies in iron cause this not to occur. Difficulties with anemia only occur after the body's stored iron is depleted.

There are several really good food sources for iron. Some of these are eggs, green vegetables, fruits, and milk. Iron is in a large variety of plants. Inorganic iron is extremely hard to absorb, which is most of the iron that you get in health food stores. Be specific when you get iron that you get chelated iron so your body can absorb it. Iron deficiency is also associated with some types of asthma.

We will move into another commonly known mineral, copper. Copper is an interesting trace mineral that should have an optimal allowance of point five (.5) to two Mg's a day. Organic copper will actually pull out other copper that is sitting in the system as a toxin. Sometimes you can get such toxicity that it actually causes a particular disease. You can identify the toxicity from the inability to get that metallic taste out of your mouth. Too much copper can cause nausea, abdominal pain, and headaches.

Be careful when taking copper that you never take too much if you have something called Wilson's disease. Copper and zinc should always be taken together. Thirty milligrams of zinc per day to two milligrams of copper will keep your zinc and copper ratio even. Zinc will take out inorganic copper that has been left in your system.

Chromium is an interesting mineral that has been used in a variety of studies for the treatment of diabetes. Chromium has been used to treat high cholesterol, especially in cases dealing with related diabetes. Hypoglycemia can be treated with chromium. Make sure when you use chromium you are not using chromium polynicotinate because you won't get the results that you want.

The mineral selenium is vital for the absorption of vitamin E. Selenium is remarkable in the treatment of cancer. It pulls out the toxicity effects of many heavy duty metal carcinogens, such as mercury, eagerly and efficiently. Selenium is used for the heart, for cancer, for mercury accumulations, and it's also used for arthritis.

The function of the thyroid is aided by the use of iodine. Foods that offer a good source of iodine are shellfish, fish, and most seafood. Most bland vegetables are rather low in iodine. One of the biggest sources of iodine for individuals, is iodized salt. Iodine has a toxic effect if you use over a thousand micrograms a day. If you take in too much iodine you form what is called an iodized goiter.

Still another mineral needed in the body is potassium. Potassium is vital to the body in maintaining the fluid balance in our cells. Potassium deficiencies usually cause terrible cramps, nausea, vomiting, weakness, muscle spasms,

rapid heartbeat, and sometimes heart failure. Like magnesium, potassium is vital for the heart. Potassium is readily available in fresh fruits and other fresh foods, such as watermelon, cream of tartar, potatoes, bananas, oranges, and tomatoes. Potassium exists in balance with the sodium in the body. Do not take more than eighteen grams a day or you could have kidney failure. Make sure you use common sense when you take it.

Let's quickly discuss something called COQ10. COQ10 is essential for the heart. It supplies the energy for the heart's pumping action. Without a sufficient supply of COQ10 your heart simply fails. The cells energy requires COQ10. All adults should be taking from 60 mg. to 100 mg. daily of this vital supplement, along with vitamin E for maximum absorption.

People who have MS usually have a deficiency of COQ10. COQ10 will benefit everyone who has MS. People who have been exposed to radiation also need to be taking COQ10.

Boron is another essential mineral. From boron we receive calcium, magnesium, and zinc. It increases bone density.

Here is an abbreviated list of illnesses and certain health problems that can be caused by mineral deficiencies. I will list the illness or problem first, then the mineral or minerals that could be lacking.

Acne: zinc and sulfur.

Anemia: iron, copper, selenium, and sometimes cobalt

Arthritis: calcium, copper, magnesium, potassium, and boron.

Asthma: magnesium, zinc, and potassium.

Birth defects: zinc, copper, selenium, magnesium and manganese.

Cancer: selenium, germanium, vitamin A, vitamin C, and vitamin E. One comment I would like to make about an alkaline body is that cancer simply can not exist in an alkaline body. And the body can be made alkaline with proper uses of calcium, which will turn the body to alkaline.

Candida: zinc, selenium, chromium, and garlic.

Diabetes: chromium, magnesium, zinc, vitamin B2, and vitamin B6

Goiter: iron and copper.

Hair loss: copper and zinc.

Hypoglycemia: chromium, vanadium, and zinc.

Immune system: chromium, selenium, and zinc.

Impotence: selenium, zinc, manganese, calcium, chromium

Menstrual cramps: calcium and sodium

Muscular Dystrophy: COQ10, selenium, potassium, and manganese.

PMS: chromium, silenium, and zinc

Sexual dysfunction: selenium, zinc, and manganese

Sexual stimulation: lecithin, damiana, selenium, and
vitamin E

There is an abundance of information available on vitamins and minerals. You can find several books filled with information on the subject. This short overview was intended to give you some ideas of the problems that can be caused by your body lack of certain vitamins and minerals.

Problems can also arise when your body is lacking certain amino acids. Certain amino acids actually help what is called the growth hormone. When you look into a person's body and see deficiencies, you can usually correct this by suggesting that they use the proper vitamins and minerals.

You must train yourself to ask the body and the Creator what specific vitamins or minerals are needed. Again, calcium was the number one mineral I have found to be deficient in most people.

Chapter Seven

Dealing with Illnesses

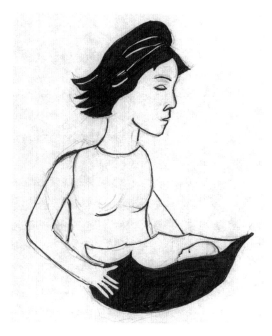

In the next chapter we're going to talk about different diseases and how to work on them, which vitamins work best with them, and how to actually do psychic work on them.

Here is a guide I have implemented to help you while working on some of the illnesses you will no doubt encounter.

After doing many seminars, and teaching a wide variety of people the healing techniques that we described in the previous chapters, we have found that there is a guideline to go by while working with these different diseases.

Cancer:

Let's start with a major illness that I am asked to address on a daily basis, cancer. Throughout history every particular healer has had his/her own idea on how to deal with this disease. I believe that cancer is actually caused by six different viruses; however, I also believe that the body is creating cancer to help us, not hurt us. In fact, I believe that the reason cancer gets out of control is simply because the body can no longer tolerate the toxins that are in it. Let me further elaborate.

Cancer cells can't communicate like other cells. They are unable to hear the cells around them to know that they are doing the wrong thing. So all they do is reproduce, over and over again. We have found many technical ways of working on cancer. One of the ways is going up and commanding that the energy field that blocks these cells from communicating with other cells, be pulled, cancelled, and replaced with the ability to hear the other cells around them.

When the cancer cells hear the other cells around them, and they know they are doing the wrong thing and are not like normal cells, they will actually destroy themselves, or turn back into normal cells.

Here's the rest of the theory. Cancer cells have receptors, special receptors that draw to them feelings of anger or hatred. This has been proven by a biochemist. Receptors are like little doorways that sit on the cell's surface and let hormones and other chemical messages in and out. Now, cancer cells have receptors that actually pull anger and hatred. They also pull toxins like crazy.

And they also pull hugh amounts of protein into their space, growing and growing in this energy. The fact is, if there is too much protein in the body, the cells will suffocate from the overdose of protein. That's right! They can't get adequate oxygen.

Number two. Toxins in the body, high levels of toxins, such as those found in mercury, are the toxins that cause cancer in the body.

Number three. Anger, hatred and sorrow are known to feed and grow cancer. So let's say the body was overdosed with major toxins, creating many different viruses. Finally, it triggers the body to do something to save itself from all these invading viruses and toxins; viruses that are caused by too much parasite activity. Parasites release waste products that the body can't get rid of. Candida releases something called acetaldehyde into the system. Metal toxins in the body are not meant to break down, they do not do so easily. When the body becomes overloaded with these toxins, it creates cells to draw these toxins to them. As these cells multiply, they are unable to clean these toxins up. The body then creates more new cells. Eventually, these extra cells become cancerous. For what it'sworth, that's the theory according to *Vianna*.

Now let me tell you how we have worked on it. First of all we have to go in and find the source of the problem. If it's a heavy metal poison, the body reacts immediately to the healing. In some cases you can actually go into the cancer and erase it like you're erasing a chalkboard, erasing the tumor completely, commanding it gone, and replacing it with normal processing cells. If a toxin is poisoning the body, and you can remove this toxin, it will erase the cancer immediately.

And there are supplements you can take to help pull these toxins out. Remember that the most important aspect in fighting cancer is to insure that the person has an alkaline body.

If the person has created a cancer from negative programs, such as I hate this person, I hate that person, or I should die, or the doctor thinks I'm going to die, you need to go in and do the four level reprogramming. Also make sure

you check every person you work on who's been diagnosed with cancer to see if he/she has the program "I believe everything that the doctors says." Many times just telling a person that he/she has cancer gives them the ability to create a slow and methodical death for themselves..

Simply because you're told you have something doesn't mean that you have to keep it. Going in and programming a person to be well on a subconscious level will make certain and insure that the body can actually take care itself. Programming them that they do not have cancer, and that they are healthy and strong will tell the subconscious to correct the problem immediately. Again, always put them on an alkaline diet, recommend a good calcium, and follow their progress.

Anytime you start working on people with cancer, you're going to run into many different feelings. People with liver cancer have an enormous amount of anger, and will suddenly begin to blame you for everything and anything. Please understand, this is not the person, this is the cancer. Go in and pull the anger and make sure that you've tested for health and strength, and program for what is needed.

Also ask the person what the cancer is doing to serve him/her. Many people will give you an actual reason, or something the cancer has done to change their life. Listen to them carefully. This is where you begin to work on the subconscious programming.

Some cancers can be healed in an instant if the cancer is caused by an emotional ailment. If a feeling is holding their cancer, test the person and see if you can find repressed anger, rejections, feelings of despair, or feelings of loneliness. Breast cancer is always connected to poor relationships. These could be relationships with siblings, mates, or parents; feelings of hopelessness, helplessness, hatred, over burdened, being unable to change what you're feeling, and wanting to get even.

You have to start from their childhood and go on from there. Pull the subconscious core beliefs that are blocking their healings. This is one of the most phenomenal and quickest ways of working on all cancers.

There are several different approaches that allow the healer to work on the cancer itself. One efficient and excellent way of working on the cancer, is to go in and listen to the sound and tones that the cancer is making, and command the opposite tone. Many times the cancer dissipates completely. Another way of working on cancer, which seems quite efficient and adequate, is to command the cancer cells to communicate with the other cells, or the healthy cells. Replacing hatred with love will help the cancer disintegrate and destroy itself.

Remember, the cancer isn't there to cause harm, cancer is actually there for another reason, at least that is what I believe. There are literally hundreds of different kinds of cancer. Science has put these illnesses in a nice little package and called them all cancer.

Prostrate cancer is usually associated with definite problems in relationships. The cancer attaches itself to the weakened area of the body, the area under distress, the area with the emotion that is out of control and out of order.

Of the different cancers that we have worked on, we have found brain cancer to be one of the most receptive to healing. It seems to be quite easy to shrink, disintegrate, and made to leave the body. Of the many different diseases known to man, cancer seems to be one of the most receptive to psychic healings.

Arthritis:

In the discussion of other illnesses such as arthritis, we have found that by taking a person off of milk products and white flour, we can usually clean out most arthritis symptoms. And at the same time putting them on a good calcium, and magnesium, zinc, and boron. Chelated calcium seems to be the best and most bioavailable of all the calciums.

Also check by muscle testing the person to see if he/she needs their core beliefs and their genetic beliefs, pulled, changed, and replaced with something different. Look for criticizing others, holding on to feelings of hostility, anger, rigid thinking, crying inside, deep sadness and sorrow.

Alcoholism:

Another common disease we need to address is alcoholism. We've found that going up and moving a person's seratonin level actually helps a person achieve more freedom from the compulsive tendencies of alcoholism. Feelings of guilt, worthlessness, rejection, all contribute to the person's tendency for being an alcoholic; however, seratonin plays a very large role. Alcoholics are naturally low in seratonin. And it is my belief that they're trying to medicate themselves on a subconscious level by using alcohol. Raising their seratonin level creates less of a need for alcohol.

Allergies:

People suffering from allergies can be helped by working on the four level belief systems. Do this by pulling each one of their different allergic reactions. Allergies are also caused by different fears, and associating a smell to something tragic that happened in their lifetime. Too much acetaldehyde in the system will also cause increased suffering if you have allergies. To counteract this I would recommend using molybdenum. Start by using 100 MG's a day, increasing to 500 MG's a day over a two month period.

Anemia:

Anemia can be worked on by adding iron and a good vitamin B complex as a supplement. Check to see if they have the ability to absorb their irons and their vitamin B's, by asking the Creator to take you to the chromosomes and show you if there is a problem in the absorption of vitamins and minerals. If there is no problem in the absorption, you simply give them the vitamin supplement they are lacking. If there is a problem in their absorption, you ask the Creator to show you what needs to be worked on in their genetic levels.

Asthma:

Asthma is a interesting illness, since asthma is held by fear. Remember the lungs are the houses where fear is stored. There, suppressed fear and "crying inside" cause asthma. Another thing that causes and effects asthma is something called acetaldehyde that gathers in the body causing breathing problems. Parasites such as worms can also cause asthma. Suggest the

person use molybdenum. MSM, which is a natural occuring sulfur and an actual part of an amino acid, is used to pull toxins out of the body. It is a phenomenal anti-oxidant that builds the bones and the body. Also, suggest the person use extra vitamin B, and of course vitamin C. Then go in and pull the different dependency issues, the over sensitive feelings of crying inside, and relieving childhood fears. Childhood fears are a learned behavior. Children learn to have asthma. Something triggers their adrenals to make them panic. Pulling out the depressed feelings and anxiety will help their asthma. Asthma can also be caused by fungas. Oregano oil, cumin and myrtle can be used to treat fungas.

Bleeding gums:

Bleeding gums is usually caused by deficiency of vitamin C. However, deficiencies in other minerals can also cause the same effect. Give the person minerals, vitamin C, have them brush their teeth, and rinse with 3 drops of melaleuca in water. This will cure their gums immediately and they will become stronger.

Blood disorders:

Blood disorders can be worked on with the genetic clip technique by asking the Creator to show you the disorder and how to correct it.

Bowel disorders:

Many bowel disorders are caused by vitamin deficiencies. Many times the ileocecal valve closes off causing a back up of toxins throughout the body. Command that the ileocecal valve open and suggest a good laxative as well as a liver flush. Magnesium is excellent for treatment of sluggish bowels.

Bladder infections:

Bladder infections are one of the easiest to clear up psychically. First find out who you're angry at, and pull the energy of "I am angry at" and replace with "I release." Other external energies may also cause bladder infections.

A bladder infection can be easily fixed by going up,

1. Making the command, "Father, Mother, God,
2. I command this bladder infection to be gone now,
3. Thank-you,
4. It is done, it is done, it is done."
5. Watch yourself go down into the bladder and scrape the bladder like you were scraping out the infection. Pull it down through the tube, out through the urethra, and throw it to God's light.

This is an extremely easy way to clean up bladder infections. Once you are able to clean up bladder infections, you will have clientele that will love you.

Broken bones:

Bones that are broken and separated can be worked on by doing the basic healing technique; going up and commanding the bone to be completely healed, watching it heal and wrapping it with calcium.

Candida:

To heal someone with candida you need to make sure the person you are working on gives up all of his/her white breads and glutton and you need to recommend they take MSM. Also you need to suggest they use Molybdenum, taking 100 micrograms a day to start, moving up to 300 micrograms a day the second week, then gradually move up to 500 micrograms a day. This will work well for this ailment. They should consider remaining on this for four months. Also, Olive leaf extract is an excellent herb for treating candida. It is anti-fungal and anti-bacterial. One of the primary feelings associated with candida, is resentment.

Carpal tunnel:

Carpal tunnel is associated with a lack of vitamin B6. After taking vitamin B6, go in and command God to stretch their tendons slowly back to where they should be. Command the nerves to grow back to normal as they were before they became injured. Then by commanding relief you should have drastically improved the carpal tunnel syndrome, if you have not alleviated it altogether.

Colon disorders:

Most colon disorders are associated with the fact that the elimination system of the body is holding too much, too long. To help colon disorders of the body you should advise them to take chelated calcium and magnesium to make sure their body is alkaline. Pull out all hatred and resentment. Make sure that the ileocecal valve is open. Suggest that they remove wheat and glutton from their diet. Another method of healing for the colon is colored light therapy. This seems to be extremely productive. Aloe is a good laxative for this.

Comas:

I would now like to discuss how to deal with a person in a coma. On many occasions when a person is in a coma you cannot awaken them because the spirit has left the body. Quite often this spirit has actually been knocked out of the body by some traumatic experience such as an accident.

The spirit knows the pain it may encounter if it returns to the body, so it avoids returning. There is even a chance the spirit may become lost while gone from the body.

Even though the spirit is gone from the body, or cannot find the body to return, there is an umbilical cord attached to this spirit. You can use this silvery umbilical cord to locate this spirit.

You can work on this person by:

1. Go up to your crown chakra.
2. Make your normal command to the Creator,
3. Go over into the person through his/her crown chakra, go down into the body and locate that silver thread attached to their spirit. Follow the thread until you find the spirit. Inform the spirit that it is out of its body, and ask it if it would like to return. If the spirit replies with an affirmative answer, return to the body, grab the umbilical cord and pull the spirit back into it's body. Tell the person to wake up slowly. You do this so you do not shock the individual by waking him/her to rapidly

4. Remember to thank the Creator.

When dealing with children who's spirit has left the body, it is vital that you remember that a child's soul, afraid of any pain, is not easy to bring back. You must be persistent with them.

Deafness:

Check his/her four level belief programs to see if they can hear. "I'm afraid to hear what's going on," is another program that must be worked on. Pull the I am afraid, and say it's ok to hear what's going on. This alone will improve the hearing. You may also go into the ear and order the reconstruction of the damaged parts. You will see what looks like little hairs start to pop up in the eardrum.

Many times you can watch the ear drum reconstruct itself. Sometimes deafness is caused by scar tissue, and when the scar tissue pulls away, you can actually watch the ear reconstruct itself. It is important that if you do not understand the way the ear is constructed, you can command it being done by going in and looking at your own ear. Then by reproducing what you see in your own ear, you can reconstruct it in another person.

If a child has never heard before, and he/she is are over twelve years of age, it is very likely that they will not be able to speak. This is because the receptors that teach speech patterns have died away by the time they're eight to twelve years old. So it very important if the child is deaf, to go in and reconstruct and command that these receptors that were there at birth, be gathered again and reconditioned. Commanding the DNA to produce these again is possible. Any cell can be taken back to fetal memory.

Death wishes:

You will be faced with people who have a death wish. These are individuals who do not want to heal what's ailing them. Quite often you will find this to be of genetic character. Go into the four levels. Program your clients to have self-love, and worthiness. For instance, check the person subconscious, muscle test them to see if they have lack of self-love, or they love themselves.

If they don't, then you pull lack of self-love, and replace it with love of self. See if they feel worthy. Have them say, "I am worthy." If it comes out "no", pull the "I am worthy, no," and replace it with, "I am worthy, yes." Check it on all four levels and replace each level as needed.

Depression:

You will find that depression and nervousness is often caused by a lack of certain vitamins. Vitamin B complexes, calcium, Royal Camu and St Johns Wort can be used against depression and nervousness. A warning here, St. John's Wort should not be used if you have hypoglycemia. Also check for fear of failure. Check for any mercury in their system that may need to be removed and raise the Seratonin level. Refer to the chapter on gene replacement.

Diabetes:

Another illness you will face is diabetes. Diabetes, seems to be held on a past life level. Start by working on the core belief level, but make sure you take it all the way to the past life and soul level.

Feelings of sorrow, emotional shock, the joy is gone in life, judgment, anger, and again diabetes, are held on a past life level.

Go in and command the chromosomes to change, causing them to produce the right amount of insulin, neurons, and the receptors that are likely to take the messages needed by the body to create the proper amounts of insulin.

You should also command the insulin level to return to the level that it was before the diabetes took hold of the body. You will also find that diabetes seems to have an interaction with a light virus over the cells which blocks them from hearing each other correctly.

Go in and pull the virus off these cells, and send it to God's light. Give the client chromium, calcium, and magnesium. With all genetic defects, where one defect is found, another one exists.

Ask the Creator to show you the other defect, and command the Creator to repair this also.

Dizziness:

Dizziness is usually caused by something going on in the inner ear. By having the Creator balance the equilibrium you can solve this problem. Dizziness can also be caused by a lack of magnesium and Vitamin B.

Endocrine system:

Moving to the endocrine system, which is the hormone producing glands of the body, you will find that they are not all controlled by the pituitary. Some are controlled by the hypothalamus. These glands work very hard to produce the hormones that our bodies need.

The endocrine system consists of the parathyroid gland, the pancreas, the adrenals, the thyroid, the hypothalamus, the heart, the kidneys, the pancreas, the stomach, the intestines, the ovaries, the sex glands, and the testes. The adrenal glands produce the steroid hormones that influence fats, proteins, carbohydrates, minerals, and other hormones. This in turn influences our body's stress level.

The thyroid produces a hormone that effects the body's metabolism, growth, heart rate, bone and general growth. Hormones act throughout the body to promote the protein synthesis essential for normal health and growth. Also attached to the hypothalamus is the pituitary. It controls many of the other glands. Each person is a totally different entity, so what works for one person may be totally different with another. Always ask God how to change his/her system!

Eyes:

Let's move on to the eyes. You need to go into the subconscious mind and program yourself, or your client, on all four levels of the core belief programming that they want to see. Also, go in and pull what is called their history memories of why they can't see. In doing the eyes you also need to do the gene clip replacement. To focus at a distance, the lens relaxes over the eyes, the muscles relax, and the lens slants and bends so the light rays go directly to the back of the eyes. The muscles contract and the eye lens

becomes more rounded.

At the point at where the image goes through the lens, the objects will become blurred, causing near sighted vision. It occurs when the lens reaches its maximum curvature. You do not have to know the structure of the eye. Imagine the light as it enters the eye hitting the back of the eye, evenly and correctly. If they are farsighted, have them look at an object in the distance. If they are somewhat near sighted have them focus on something close at hand as you correct the light entrances into their eye. Stay with it and watch it till the light actually hits the back of their eye in the correct position.

Sometimes the eye refuses to correct completely. This means that there is too much emotion for the mind to deal with. Eyes usually will not correct instantly. Your body may not be able to handle this. You will bring up other emotions as the eyes heal. A gradual improvement is much easier for your system. When dealing with the eyes, check the belief systems for fear of seeing the truth and, "I am a victim." As always, if you have any questions here, go up and ask God.

To pull off a cataract, you need to go into the eye and imagine the cataract being scraped off the eye. Glaucoma causes blindness due to increased pressure within the eye. This is caused by a blockage in the blood flow to the optic nerve. The result is the degeneration of nerve fibers. Go into the eye and help increase the blood flow to the eye by opening the capillaries. This is the most successful way to work on glaucoma.

Again nearsightedness occurs when the eyeball is too long. Instead of focusing on the retina's surface, the image is focused in front of it. You need to re-adjust this part of surface until you are able to make the focus correctly.

Remember, farsightedness occurs when the eyeball is too short, causing the image to focus behind the retina instead of on the surface. You can correct this by changing the surface of the eye. Always work on the eye on a genetic level too, so the eye work that you do will hold and stay. In a weird kind of way you're going to be like an eye surgeon by actually moving the way the light hits the surface of the eye, and making sure that it hits the back of the eye correctly. By having the light hit directly at the very back of the eye, in a perfect line, you will improve the eyesight.

Fiberic tumors:

Fiberic tumors can be changed easily by adding more calcium to the diet and using a liver cleanse. Go in and work on the fibroids by telling them to go away. Make sure that you work on any unresolved hurts of the person. By giving them calcium you will shrink their fibroids. MACA, an herb from South America, will shrink their fibroids also. If they're biting their fingernails, consider this another indication that their body might be needing calcium

Gallstones:

For gallstones, you can obtain many gallstone cleanses and liver cleanses that can help. You can also go in and command them to break down into small pieces. This method can be used also for kidney stones as well as the gallbladder stones.

Heart:

When dealing with the hurt and broken heart, and your client is complaining about heartache, you will need to reprogram them to accept love easily. If after seeking the Creators wisdom, you feel that it is a physical problem with the heart, go in and clean out all the valves in the heart area, intuitively with your mind. Give them a detoxin of magnesium and a mineral supplement. Keep an eye on him/her. Be prepared to work on their heart when it needs to be worked on.

Hepatitis:

When working on hepatitis we have found it very effective to pull the hepatitis virus itself, or to change the virus by mimicking the exact tone of the virus and then commanding it to go exactly opposite. To do this, you go up and say, "Father, Mother, God, show me the tone of this virus. Father, Mother, God I command it too be replaced with the opposite tone," and the virus disappears completely.

At the same time you can go in and pull one atom out of the molecular structure of the cell of the virus, and the virus will fade away. We have experienced very good results with hepatitis.

Also, put them on milk thistle and have them continue with the milk thistle. And obviously, start anyone who is having problems on a liver cleanse.

Hypoglycemia:

Hypoglycemia is usually caused by an allergic reaction to glutton. Individuals suffering from hypoglycemia need to be programmed to have joy with life. And they need to eliminate most of their white breads from their diet. Also, chromium and calcium will help.

Incontinence:

Incontinence usually happens when the bladder has slipped and the kidneys are weak. Build the kidney up with the herb, juniper berries. Imagine the bladder being pulled up. This is another malady I feel can be improved with a liver cleanse. When the kidneys are in a weakened condition they do not absorb calcium as readily as they should. The liver cleanse will help this situation

Insomnia:

Insomnia is usually caused by lack of magnesium. Sometimes the person may lack other vitamins too, but ask the Creator. Go in and pull feelings of anxiety and fear. Go in and stimulate more Seratonin, and the release of something called melatonin.

Kidneys:

Kidney problems arise when you're very upset, when you're over judgmental, and when you're angry with people. Anger is stored in the kidneys. So if you're really angry, it effects the kidneys. Kidney stones are caused by the lack of minerals in the body.

Going in and imagining the kidney stones breaking up and exploding into small tiny pieces is a very effective way to remove kidney stones. Act upon a kidney infection the same way you would a bladder infection, scraping the infection out of the kidneys, pulling it down and out of the body.

You may advise your clients to use Breakstone Tea to help with kidneys, as well as the liver cleanse.

Knees:

Knee problems create a substantial amount of work for healers. Ask the Creator where you need to go into the knee to put the knee back where it should be, and put the knee back in place. Scrape out any excess deposits if need be.

Always clarify which knee needs to be worked on as you may be mistaken which side of the body you are observing. The left knee may have something to do with the feminine side. The right knee is their lack of desire for wanting to go forward. You will find that there is a direct correlation between the knees and the kidneys.

The Liver:

The liver is responsible for over five hundred functions in the body. The liver produces cholesterol and bile from the breakdown of dietary fat and old red blood cells. Using amino acids, it makes proteins and stores iron, glycogen , and vitamins. It also removes substances such as poisons and waste products from the blood, excreting or converting them to safer substances.

When the liver becomes inundated with toxins, it can no longer function correctly. This in turn will cause imbalances in your hormones that regulate sexual behavior, growth, and the flow of serotonin. The Taoists teach that if the liver and kidneys are clean, man will not age. Due to all of the toxins and pollutions in our environment, our livers are overworked. If your liver is functioning, your body will be strong and healthy.

To keep the gallbladder and liver functioning correctly, I offer you the excellent liver cleanse listed below. Read the instructions carefully, and of course, go up and ask God is this is right for you.

Gallbladder/Liver Cleanse!

1. <u>First day of cleanse.</u> Take an herbal laxative in the evening.

2. <u>Each morning for the next three days.</u> (Day 2-4) Place one hundred (100) drops of Ortho-Phos in a quart of high-quality apple juice and drink during the morning. During these three days you do not need to alter your diet. If for some reason you can not drink apple juice, place 135 drops of Ortho-Phos in a quart of water and drink during the morning. These drops are the basis of the cleanse, if you do not want to take the drops do not participate in this program. So overall you are going to take 3 quarts of apple juice and 300 drops during this 3 day period.

#3. <u>Evening of the fourth day.</u> Eat supper at a fairly early time. Then about an hour before your normal bedtime <u>take a cup of olive oil, a cup of coke, and 1 whole lemon squeezed.</u> Use a high-quality olive oil, one that is cold pressed. Stir these three ingredients together and drink. The coke is used to help swallow the olive oil. Without the coke, the olive oil is very hard to swallow. You will find the coke and lemon make the olive oil almost tasteless.

#4. <u>Immediately after you drink the olive oil mixture, go to bed.</u> Put your knees up to your chest. <u>Lie on your right side for half an hour.</u> This will cause the oil to go directly to the gallbladder and liver. These organs will not know what to do with all that oil, so they will spasm and throw off stones. Then you are free to get up and do as you wish. By taking this oil mixture you empty the system of its old bile, making new bile. The system, which normally recycles its bile, is forced to make new bile without the old toxins.

#5. <u>Take an herbal laxative the next morning.</u> This will help flush the stones out of the colon. Actually, you should do this step <u>before</u> you begin the program. The cleaner your colon is the easier it is to flush stones.

#6. <u>Consider taking a colonic two days after the flush.</u>

#7. <u>Frequency.</u> If you are very sick, (such as cancer), consider doing this once a month for a few months. Everyone's system is different; therefore there are no absolute rules. For prevention, repeat this cleanse at least once a year.

Note:Ortho-Phoscanbepurchased from HarvestMoonNatural Foods, 2113-A E. 151 Street, Olathe, KS 66062, (913) 782-7562. Ortho-Phos is a brand name for ortho-posphoric acid.

Epsom Salt Variation

The Epsom salt keeps the bowels moving so any remaining toxins are not left in the body causing ill side effects.

1. <u>Take two tablespoons of Epsom salt.</u> On the third day of the liver flush, two hours after lunch, dissolve two tablespoons of Epsom salt in three ounces of water and drink. If you find the taste intolerable, add a little citrus juice.

#2. <u>Evening dose.</u> Five hours after lunch dissolve one tablespoon of Epsom salt in three ounces of water and drink.

#3. <u>The next morning.</u> Take one tablespoon of Epsom salt dissolved in three ounces of water and drink it.

Note to reader, this cleanse is intended as an informational guide. The remedy, approaches, and technique described herein are meant to supplement, and not to be a substitute for, professional medical care or treatment. It should not be used to treat a serious aliment without prior consultation with a qualified healthcare professional.

The drops for this cleanse are carried at a variety of health food stores. If you can not find a source, please call Natures Path at (208) 524-0808.

Leukemia:

Leukemia is caused in most cases by mercury poisoning. Make sure you pull the mercury out of the body. Go in and tell the body to produce the right red blood cells. In some cases of leukemia, the body is producing too many red baby blood cells, and the white blood cells are trying to get rid of them. Go in and make sure the red blood cells are correct and proper and that the white blood cells accept them.

Command the leukemia to be gone, the body to be healed. Quite often in leukemia you will find mercury. Pull this mercury out of the body by giving coriander. Pull out all silver fillings when dealing with leukemia. Liver flushes and selenium are excellent weapons against leukemia.

Lungs:

The lungs are responsible for feelings such as grief and sorrow. Anything correlated or associated with the lungs has to do with great sorrow, pain, and fear. All fear breeds sorrow. Talk to the person to find out what their life is like and what is going on in their life, and commence helping them to release some of the grief.

Sorrow is one of the major emotions. You may not be able to completely change their sorrow, but you can pull out the program that they have to have grief, and that love hurts. Changing these things in their lungs will change their life immediately. Also, one thing that effects the lungs probably more than anything else we have ever noticed, is the lack of water.

A lack of water seems to make the person asthmatic, causing major problems in the lung area. Make sure you give them enough water to hydrate them. Some of the water that we drink will not hydrate since the molecular structure of the water goes in the opposite direction that it should. This is caused by the direction the water spins as it goes through the plumbing.

To counter this effect, hold your water in your hands before you drink it; see the molecules shift to the different direction. You may also hold a magnet on the side of your cup to change the rotation of the water. This will allow you to absorb the water with less difficulty.

Menstrual Cramps:

For menstrual cramps and most all other cramps, suggest chelated calcium and magnesium. For those who complain of charley horses, suggest calcium, potassium, magnesium, and vitamin E. Damiana has a lot of healthy calcium in it, plus it balances the hormones; howver, it will deplete the iron in your system, so anyone taking Damiana should take it with black strap molasses.

Menopause:

Menopause can be helped along by telling the body to go into full menopause--the whole process-- instead of letting the body fight itself.

Migraine Headaches:

Next lets talk about a very painful issue, migraine headaches. Three things cause migraine headaches. One, your neck may be out of place. Two, it can be hormonal. And three, it may be just absolute total stress. The first thing you need to do is find the cause. If it's hormonal, based around a woman's menstrual cycle, you can suggest several different remedies.

Dandelion is one that I recommend because it cleans some of the hormones out of the liver, aids with PMS, and actually helps with migraines. I find that three to four cycles of the liver cleanse also helps. Always go in and move the neck back to where it should be. You can also give relief to a migraine headache with either a coffee enema or with caffeine.

A hot bath laced with Epsom salts or a massage is an excellent way to relieve the migraines, if the cause is stress. You should understand that a migraine is not exactly a headache, but is caused by the way the blood is flowing to the brain.

Obesity:

Let's discuss a major issue found everywhere. Being overweight is now considered a national problem, and it is a problem that you will be asked to solve on a continuing basis. Always start by making sure that you program the person that they are thin. You can make a major change in their diet just by taking a person off all white bread and glutton.

I would recommend for your further studies on this subject, that you read a book by Dr. Peter J. D'Adamo called, "Eat Right for Your Type." This book not only deals with weight loss, but also deals with what you should and should not eat according to your blood type. However, the re-programming seems to bring the most phenomenal results in the end. If people come back and complain that they are gaining their weight back, make sure that you didn't program them to lose the weight, because if you did, they will find the weight again.

Always program them to release the weight. Program them with, "Every bite I eat is full of love, and I get full easy." Check the history and genetic level for beliefs that being overweight meant wealth, power, or safety. (Refer to chart) Many of the issues you will face deal with females only, evolving around the feelings of guilt, abuse, ancestral programs that sex is shameful, and feelings of guilt dealing with sexual energy. These need to be changed and put back into place. Also, stimulating the pituitary to make the correct hormones can alter the hormones.

Osteoporosis:

Osteoporosis is always associated with the lack of calcium; however, the body's inability to digest calcium, causes the calcium itself to contribute to the Osteoporosis. Always recommend they take a good calcium, and by that I mean a chelated calcium. And, always make certain to go up and check their parathyroid. This gland is responsible for telling the calcium where to go. The parathyroid gland tells the body whether to absorb it in the muscles or the bone.

Go through the body, check and ask the Creator if they have too much calcium in their blood. If they do, the parathyroid is not working correctly. Concerning feelings and emotions, the parathyroid is associated with the thyroid in not being able to defend yourself and not able to speak up and say how you truly feel. Go in and program the person to be able to say what he/she truly feels, what they truly mean. Always check here to make sure the kidneys are functioning correctly.

Parasites:

You can rid the body of most parasites found in the United States by using black walnut, clove, and wormwood. However, if the persons have traveled abroad, or has been to Mexico, you need to give them oil of oregano, and if they need oil of oregano, give them three to six drops a day, depending of the severity of the condition.

Ask the Creator how many drops of oil of oregano they need a day. Have them put it in a capsule so that they don't have to taste the potency of oregano, or have them mix the oregano in a glass of water. Oregano will attack and destroy any parasite that is in the human body. Another item that will kill parasites is olive leaf extract. Olive leaf extract will not only kill parasites, it will also kill Canadida. If you're going to give them molybdenum, I usually give them olive leave extract also. I find the olive leaf extract to be a phenomenal herb. Hana Kroger Products have some excellent parasite remedies. Check for these products at your local health food store.

Pleurisy:

Give them the herb Pleurisy Root to help them with their pleurisy. Pleurisy is caused by the person coughing so hard that they pull the pleural lining away from their lungs. Always work on the coughing problem before you work on the pleurisy. Pleurisy is an inflammation which can be rectified by commanding that the inflammation go away and the lining of the lungs re-attach itself.

Sinus Trouble:

Sinus trouble is usually associated with someone who is being irritated by a person that is really close to him/her. However, sinus trouble can be caused by too much acetaldehyde in the system. You need molybdenum to pull out the acetaldehyde and change their allergies.

Sinus problems are often associated with teeth. Go up and ask the Creator if the person has any infected teeth. You will find that dental problems are at the root of many of the illnesses you will be presented with.   Too much histamine can cause a problem. Good muscle building exercises will help create cortisone and block the histamines. COQ10 and Licorice Root will help.

Skin Problems:

Most problems associated with the skin, acne and psoriasis topping the list, are associated with the liver. By putting the person on a good liver cleanse, you will find that their skin will clear up. Your clients may need to take the liver cleanse more than once.

Suggest that they continue to repeat the cleanse until you notice there is a difference in the complexion of the skin. Also, Molybdenum is an excellent supplement to give those suffering from skin problems. Olive leaf extract is good for skin problems attributed to acidic conditions--alkaline ph is needed.

Stroke:

Stroke is commonly associated with the lack of basic minerals, like selenium. The stroke actually makes a person feel a little rejected. A person who has suffered a stroke sometimes loses mobility of certain body parts; some of the neurons are actually no longer in existence.

Go in and program the brain back to it's original self. Or go in and start to wake up the neurons of the brain and you will have extremely good results. Make sure you put the person on the minerals selenium and vitamin E.

Teeth:

It is possible to command the DNA to reproduce a hormone to make the teeth grow in certain places. We have successfully grown back a certain tooth.

Venereal Diseases:

Venereal diseases are responsive to being worked on in much the same way as you would a viral infection. Herpes seems to be extremely receptive after you pull the persons fear of relationships and feeling that sex is wrong. Usually herpes has an episode of erupting right when the relationship seems to be getting serious or getting stronger. This causes a fear of the new relationship.

With respect to aids, HIV is extremely responsive to being worked on. AIDS itself feels almost like a negative entity. And we haven't quite figured out exactly how to keep the AIDS down the way we want to yet, but we will. HIV will responds by bringing up the T-count, making the T-count resistant to the disease. This makes the body produce more T-cells resistant to the disease. Also get the tone to the disease so the other cells can hear it.

That's right, making the tone of the disease AIDS louder so that the cells can hear it will help the cells fight it. HIV slips into the cells by mimicking DNA structure, or the cell structure of the cells. Causing the HIV tone to sound slightly different makes the HIV cells more susceptible to the cells that are fighting it. We have achieved some very good results with HIV.

Viral Infections:

Viruses either have DNA or RNA. They do not have both. They must have a host cell to remultiply. Command the virus to separate from host cell, then command the tone to destroy it. The tone will be the opposite tone from that of the virus.

These are just a few of the diseases you will encounter, and some of the things that you can do to treat them. Anytime you encounter a disease that you do not understand; you can always go up and ask Creator. This information is for use in your healing abilities.

However, once again I must remind you that we are not licensed doctors. If you feel there is a major medical problem present, never hesitate to advise your clients to seek regular medical advice.

Here is an abbreviated list of some of my favorite herbs and vitamins and the health problems that can be benefited by their use.

Acidophilus: Maintains normal bacteria balance in the intestines, lowers cholesterol, aids digestion of milk products.

Aloe Vera : Stomach disorders, high vitamin C, ulcers, constipation, arthritis.

Apple Juice: The pectin found contained in apple juice removes toxins and metals, lowers cholesterol, heart diseases, gallstones.

Bay Berry: Stimulates the intestinal movement, slows breathing, bronchial constriction.

Bee Pollen: Good source of vitamin C-amino acids-fatty acids-calcium- magnesium-potassium--fatigue, depression, cancer, colon disorders, allergies, cancer (keep in mind that if you are counseling cancer patients or are giving someone a protein supplements, bee pollen contains high amounts of protein)

Bilberry: Viruses, benefits capillaries and aids in function of the eye.

Black Cohosh: Lowers blood pressure-cholesterol levels, reduces mucus, cardiovascular system, relieves hot flashes

Black Walnut: Parasites, fungal infections

Burdock Root: Gout symptoms, blood purifier, gall bladder

Camu: Very potent anti-viral, anti-migraine, and anti-depressant

Carrot Juice: Good overall source for vitamins, cancer fighter

Cascara Sagrada: Cleans the valves, laxative for constipation, parasites

Cats Claw: Cleans intestinal tract, anti-oxidant, intestinal problems, cancer, tumors

Catnip: Natures own Alka-Seltzer, mild sedative effect on the nervous system, help prevents miscarriage, pain reliever, worms, and nerves.

Cayenne Pepper: Circulation, bleeding ulcers, arthritis

Chamomile: A gentle pain reliever, which can be given to infants, also good for relaxation.

Chaparral: Great anti-cancer supplement, is a strong anti-oxidant, good for use on tumors, antiseptic, and is able to pull LSD out of the body. Also helps purify the blood

Chinese Ma Huang: Asthma, colds, respiratory problems, heart disorders, (it is commonly referred to as Ephedra in the United States) (when given with Guarana it becomes a strong stimulant that can be dangerous.)

Chorella: Excellent source of chlorophyll-carbohydrates-vitamin C-vitamin E-proteins, bleeding gums, infections, burns, asthma, one of the best sources for pulling mercury toxins from the body (must start with small doses and increase slowly)

COQ10: Heart, cellular energies, stimulant, anti-aging

Damiana: Excellent hormone regulator. Increases fertility in both male and females.

Dandelion Root: Cleanses the blood stream and liver, protection of

bile, diuretic, help kidneys-pancreas-spleen-stomach, age spots

Echinacea: Stimulates white blood cells, anti-inflammatory, immune system, lymphatic system, colds, flues, general infections

Feverfew: Arthritis, fever, headaches, muscle tension, pain reliever, increase blood platelets,anti-inflamatory

Fenugreek: Lymphatic system, inflammation, and lungs

Flaxseed Oil: Excellent source of vitamin B-C-protein-magnesium-potassium-fiber, pain reducer, inflammation, arthritis, liver functions

Garlic Powder: Anti-biotic, anti-fungal, anti-oxidant, lowers blood pressure

Ginger Root: Cleanses the colon, reduces spasms, anti-oxidant

Ginkgo Biloba: Brain functions, pulls toxins, Alzheimer's-Parkinson's disease

Golden Seal: Anti-inflammatory, anti-bacteria, strengthening the immune system. Do not use with any disfunctions in insulin or blood sugars. Note, do not give to small children

Grape Seed Extract: Anti-oxidant, cancer treatment, toxin removal

Green Tea: Antioxidant, cancer prevention, lowers cholesterol, reduces clotting, weight loss, regulates blood sugar

Guarana: Pure form of caffeine-often used with Chinese Ma Hung-not a good combination, beware when buying or using this, that this combination should not be used

Irish Moss: Will eliminate dead tissue in the body. It is an excellent source of iodine.

Kava Kava: Depression, insomnia, stress, and urinary infections

Kelp: Good source of iodine-vitamin D, helps the heart-thyroid, high blood pressure, constipation

Licorice: Stomach problems, colon cleanse, allergic reactions, asthma, depression, fever, the bowels

Maca: For women: extra energy, PMS, menopausal symptoms, hot flashes, vaginal dryness, the "blues", postmenopausal symptoms, and healthy bones for men: enhanced libido, sexual potency, fertility, energy, and stamina

Marshmallow: Soothes-helps skin, bladder infections, kidney problems

Milk Thistle: Liver cleanse-reconstruction (not to be given in the spring because the liver is purging itself during springtime)

Olive Leaf Extract: Parasites, yeast infections, immune system

Oregano: Tapeworms

Parsley: Stimulant, worms, bladder functions, kidney functions, lungs, thyroid

Peppermint Leaves: Nausea, chills, headaches, and diarrhea

Pumpkin Seeds: Tape worms

Red Clover: Antibiotic, blood purifier, HIV, cleaning the lungs, valve disorders, liver diseases weakened immune systems.

Safflower Powder: Neutralizes uric acid, digestion of the colon, blood cleanses

Saw Palmetto: Prostate enlargement, some prostrate cancers, diuretic, urinary antiseptic, appetite stimulant

Siberian Ginseng: Strengthens the adrenal-reproduction glands, immune system, stimulates appetite, bronchitis, circulatory problems, diabetes, infertility, stress, (not to be given to small children because of the high amounts of hormones)

Slippery Elm: Lungs, urinary tract, mucus membranes, throat

Spiralina: Concentrated source of iron-proteins-amino acids, source of chlorophyll, immune system, pulls sicknesses-toxins- poisons

White Oak Bark: Good for nasal polyps. Also an anti-bacterial.

White Willow Bark: Nature's aspirin performs all functions of aspirin

Valerian Root: Blood circulation, sedative, mucus from colds, fatigue, blood pressure, irritable bowel syndrome, trace minerals required for body fluids-blood, nerve functions

Yellow Dock Root: Purifier and cleanser, improves colon-liver functions.

Yucca Root: Arthritis, osteoporosis, blood purification – liver cleanse, helps the body produce it's own cortisone.

I have provided this list of vitamins and minerals because as healers we are allowed to use any means that helps the client. Psychic healing is very effective and it works extremely well. Adding herbs and vitamins to someone's diet also gives a person control of his/her own illness. Taking these herbs and vitamins shows the subconscious that they truly want to get better. I have found that recommending ways that people can help themselves actually helps them to heal because it allows them to feel that they are doing their own healing. They feel like they are taking control of their disease.

One thing I have found; however, is that anyone who has a problem or an illnesses, needs to write a goal stating what they're going to do when they've finished with the sickness. More often than not, when people are finished with the illness and the cancer is gone, or whatever problem they had, they will look at me and say, "Now what?" They've spent so many years working on their own illnesses that they have no idea what to do next. Always encourage people think about and plan for the future.

These various things that we have discussed will help you on your healing journey, either for yourself or others. The Creator can change anything in an instant. So don't be thinking that it can't, or, that you dont have the ability or the capability to work with these technques.

I always find it most amusing when people make the remark that spiritual healing will not work, yet when they are in deep distress, they do not hesitate to petition their Creator at night in their prayers, or, when they find themselves in a difficult situation, they continue to ask, "God help me." Yet these same people don't accept that God can heal and change things in a instant. I believe those who are against faith healing, are against God. Think about it for a minute. My Creator can be measured in scientific terms, in the different brain waves and different links of communication.

Pictures can be taken of your aura and the energy you emit from your body. They can measure the weight of a soul as it leaves the body, by weighing the body before and after death.

Some say that God doesn't exist! You know, science can duplicate air; they can make an exact copy, but they can not give it to people to breathe for long periods of time, because they will die. They are unable to copy the life force. This life force can be tapped into at any time by lowering your brain waves down to theta and plugging in. The more you practice it, the more proficient you become and the more confidence you will build in yourself

Our body consists of more than just matter, or cells running around blindly communicating with each other. The cells in our bodies are very aware of the environment both inside and outside the body. Feelings, emotions, beliefs, and programs affect how we behave, and have dramatic effects on the body's well being in this world. Our experiences are important to us. Let's resolve make this life an adventure in living. Let's turn this struggle into an absolutely wonderful challange. As you become a master at doing your own healings, you will become a master of your own life.

Chapter Eight
Guardian Angels

Next on the agenda is the wonderful subject of guardian angels. You will find during this discussion that the same basic techniques already used in this text can be employed to discover our guardian angels.

When working with guardian angles you are going to use basically the same 4 steps we have already discussed, with two additional steps.

1. "Father, Mother, God,
2. Command to see this person's guardian angels.
3. Thank you.
4. It is done, it is done, it is done."
5. Go into their heart chakra from their crown.
6. Look at the aura around their shoulders and head.

To see a guardian angel, the practitioner goes up above his/her head, three, six, or sixty-seven feet to their crown chakra, and commands, "Father, Mother, God, I command to see this persons guardian angels. Thank you. It is done, it is done, it is done."

You will then go over to the recipients crown chakra, down into their heart chakra, and from that point you then pull yourself up even with their shoulders. At this time you will see the first thing that comes into your mind. You will see in your mind's eye, either balls of light or a person face. If you see balls of light, tell the person that you see two or three balls of light representing that number of guardian angels. You then command to see their faces.

If you see the faces, describe to them the faces that you are seeing. If you do not see faces, immediately command that the faces become clearer. The faces that you will observe are your client's guardian angel. This is an interesting technique. Everyone has at least two to four heavenly companions at their side.

We have tried several experiments on this technique. During one of these we had a healer observe a client's guardian angels. Immediately afterwards we had another healer check the same person to see what guardian angels they would observe. Afterwards we compared their notes. By comparing the descriptions of the faces they had both seen, we were certain they had observed the same faces. This, along with several other experiments, confirms

that the event is real. I've had so many experiences with guardian angels that they are almost too numerous to count.

These angels stand near and keep vigilence of your life. I have found guardian angels in every person, in every religion and nationality known to man. Every single one of these guardian angels has a particular name and a particular energy. I have learned that they are not always compatible and they may disagree with each other if they are guarding the same person.

However, I have come to realize that they have only the best interest of the person at heart. I know for a fact that they are real.

For example, in one particular instance, a woman came into my shop and I told her that she had a female spirit watching over her. This spirit was her guardian angel. The guardian angel said to me "I know this woman, I held her when her son died." So I told the woman her guardian angel had held her when her son had died and the woman began to cry. It seems her son had died years before the reading, and when he died she was so upset and so overshadowed with grief, that she went to her room and wept uncontrollably. While she was weeping and grieving so sadly, she felt as if someone's arms were around her and gently rocking her back and forth. She will never forget the experience.

It was all the proof that I needed to know that guardian angels were definitely there for our benefit. I have found that the number is between two to four guardian angels per person. Although they may be surrounded by many guides and many people that are interested in teaching other things, they are usually surrounded by only two to four guardian angels.

Guardian angels never leave a person unless the person passes a death door/declines an open door to go home to God--our spirits are allowed to do this. We are given many opportunities throughout life to go home. Angels may also leave when you go through what is called "the dark night of the soul," at which time the guardian angels are replaced with another set of guardian angels that will be there to walk the person's life with them.

It is important to know that guardian angels are always there. Perhaps they should be called heavenly companions, but they are there. You are never alone.

Sitting in front of a mirror or going into a moment of silence, you can go up and see your own guardian angels by using these same steps.

If at any time you see a small guardian angel, or guide, who appears to you to be around two years old, you are probably observing a child waiting to come into their life. They appear on the left side of the person, your right side if you are facing them. An individual's grandchildren can also appear.

These spirits and guides are visions that are not quite changeable as far as readings go. Enjoy this exercise. If you ask them a question, they will answer you. But always seek all of your guidance from God, and always check all your answers with God, because angels and spirit guides have their own opinions as to what is right or wrong. Even though they have your best interest at heart, you need to check their answers with God.

Chapter Nine

Waywards, Spirits,
Psychic Hooks, & Implants.

Now that you've had a pretty good orientation covering the basic healing strategies, we're going to delve into an entirely different subject. This one is called Waywards. If you can not accept this information as being true, we urge you to simply disregard it. Waywards is a word that I picked up from a wonderful woman named Barbara Hughs, who lives in Idaho. Barbara is a retired school teacher who spends much of her life pulling discontented spirits off of people--along with the other work she does. You must observe this gifted healer to know exactly how and what she does, because the people she works on get better very quickly.

A wayward spirit is a spirit that has left the body at death and doesn't know where to go. Our lives are built on a grid system, a grid system of the universe. We all live under this grid pattern. The grid system is so real that even NASA waits for what is called a window before they send their ships into space, so they can arrive at the destination they are seeking.

We are totally connected to God at all times. We are granted many windows and doors, which may allow us to go back to the Creator. When these doors come up, allowing us to pass on after death, sometimes we are afraid to go on.

Many Native American teachings show that some spirits were afraid that if they went to the light, they would lose their identity and become part of the light. This made them feel like they needed to stay on the earth to protect the earth and keep their identity.

Other people in different religious sects believe that if they committed suicide they would be tortured so badly that they were also afraid to go to the light, and refused to go. Others who have been killed in tragic deaths, such as murders or freak accidents, become so disoriented, or so upset at how their deaths occurred, that they don't take their window of light. These windows stay open about nine days after their death.

When they miss this window of light, the grid system passes by and they are trapped by the magnetic pull of the earth, so their spirits are left to walk this planet. God has not abandoned these individuals; God's time is totally different from our time. Even though we feel Ithat we've have been here for a long time, in God's time it has been a very short time.

We are all still connected to the light by a small beam of light like a thread dangling through the grid. If you were capable, you would see that connection as a pulsating light around your body. Spirits search for the light to use as a guiding beacon for the path to return to God. This light is visible for three to four days after their death. If they do not use the light to return during this period of time, their connection to God is lost.

They have in all essence lost their way. If they decide not to return back to God, then they return back to the house or the place they were before their death and they remain there. This is why they may be attracted to you. They can use your light as a pathway back to the Creator through the grid. Many times they will attach themselves to you and feed off of your energy.

These discontented spirits are called Waywards; they are easy to send to the light, because you are still connected to the grid system. They can use your grid system to go to the light. And even though you don't have a window, you are still connected to the light. So what you need to do is go above yourself and say, "Father, Mother, God, I command this spirit to go to God's light now. Thank you. It is done, it is done, it is done."

These disembodied spirits are so common that they are used in many religious practices. Send the spirits to the light, God will sort it out. They will use your connection to God to get there and they will go straight to the light.

Now this brings us to another group; they are called the fallen. They are a little different from waywards. They are spirits and entities that shouldn't be here on the earth. They are a little bit nastier than regular waywards. To work with this type, you need to go up and ask Father, Mother, God to tell you their names, and then using their names you command them to go to the light. So suppose that the spirit's name was Jo Ho Hause. You command Jo Ho Hause to go to the light now. Thank you. It is done, it is done, it is done. It is nature's law, they must now go.

Are wayward spirits real? Oh, absolutely. We've gone to many haunted houses, (it's sort of a hobby of mine) and pulling up wayward spirits and sending them to the light is rather easy; they have to listen. As long as you go above your head and go into theta, calling upon God, you're now plugged

in. They have to listen; it is a law that the waywards will not break. They will go to the light. You command them to go to the light now, and so it is, and it is done. Once they go to the light, they have gone through a filtering process and you can call upon them and speak with them.

All waywards, spirits and entities of any kind have to listen to this command. Which brings us to our two other subjects, psychic hooks and implants.

Psychic Hooks:

A psychic hook can happen anytime that you feel sympathy for someone or have strong feeling towards another person.   When you feel sorry for someone, you take part of your energy and release it to him or her. Psychic hooks are real. There have been many tests conducted where scientists have found that there is energy going from the mother to her child when the child is lying ill in the hospital. These are called fragments. The mother is feeding the child, of her own free will and accord, parts of her energy.

If we as healers begin to feel sorry for all of the people we work on, we will expend so much energy we will no longer be able to work on anyone. The idea is to feel compassion, and not sorrow, for all the people you will be associated with. These individuals are creating their own lives. Feeling compassion, going in and helping them is better than sitting on the bench whining and crying with them. However, even the best of us, can get what is called a psychic hook.

Psychic hooks evolve from relationships and people we've been with. To pull off the psychic hook, you need to go up above yourself and say, "Father, Mother, God, I command that all hooks be pulled, cancelled, and released back to the person that sent them, and pull mine back also. Thank you, It is done, it is done, it is done."

Another way of pulling back psychic hooks is to call back all the soul fragments that you have received, or that you've given to other people, giving them back their soul fragments that you have received from them and taking back all the soul fragments that you've given.   For instance, in a sexual relationship that you've been involved in previously, such as an ex-husband or

ex-wife, or perhaps a rape situation, or maybe something even as small as a gripe that a father or mother still have over their children, you go up above yourself and say, "Father, Mother, God, I command that all soul fragments be pulled from other people that I have given, pulled, washed off and returned to me, and that all their soul fragments be pulled from me, be washed off, and returned to them. Thank you. It is done, it is done, it is done."

Pulling these psychic hooks is an excellent psychic exercise. It will do incredible things for your strength. If you, as a woman, still think about that ex-husband that you had ten years ago, there's a reason for it. You still carry a fragment. Please understand, there's nothing wrong with thinking about that person, but make sure that you are not continuing to give your power away, and that you're not taking their power from them.

Next we come to what I call implants. Some people may feel that when we speak about implants, we are talking about something that is on a psychic level. When I say implant, I mean that we have actually found metal implants in people. I just call them implants. They could be alien implants or government implants, who knows, it doesn't matter.

Wherever the people get them from, they need to be removed. If you're going to do psychic work, there's a very good chance that you will pull some of these people to you. Some of them you may just regard as fruitcakes, and that's ok; however, there are some who are real. You will know when you touch them if they are telling you the truth.

Government implants are implants I have found on men who work for different government sites or government institutions, and women who are very intuitive and very psychic. I have never found one on other than this group of people. Are they from our government? I don't know. But I know that they are real, and I know that I have my own theories and my own opinions, which I do not wish to share at this time. However, to pull them out of people, you need to go up above your space, and ask the Creator for the tone that will destroy the implant.

How real are they? Well, my husband came into the shop one day, and while he was there, a lady came in with a large bulge protruding from her arm. She could feel a round object in the bulge. The object was hard. You could feel it as well as see it. After I commanded the tone that would destroy the object, the object disappeared and faded away. My new husband was stunned as he watched it fade away. This was real! While working on people with implants, go up, ask the tone to destroy the implants, then destroy them.

Chapter Ten

Animals

I would like to now address a topic that may cause some of you to wonder why I have included it at all, while others may find this the most exciting portion of the book, The topic concerns animals and how to work with them.

When you "go in" to speak with an animal, you need to realize that basically, animals do not understand the spoken word. A much more realistic way to communicate with an animal is to form a picture and then transfer it to the animal's mind.

For example, if you have a dog that is depressed and lethargic, you should project the picture of the animal in a happy situation, with the master as its friend, giving it love.

It is important to know that an animal will instinctively take on the disease of its master in an attempt to "cure" or "take away" the illness as a gesture of unconditional love.

You will find that orchestrating a healing for an animal is much the same as the procedures we have been using, except for a few key points.

By nature, animals tend to to try and absorb their master's illnesses. Once they do so, they are unable to rid these illnesses from themselves. Send these illnesses to the earth, or to the light. By sending these illnesses to either the earth or the light, you will change the negative energy in the animal to usable energy.

It is also very important to understand that sending a feeling is much different than sending words. You are sending an emotion to the animal, not spoken words.

If you find yourself in a situation where you feel threatened by an animal, do not project the thought, "do not bite me." Projecting any kind of image about biting may be misinterpreted, and you could cause a biting incident. Instead, if you find yourself in a situation with an aggressive animal, project pure love to the animal, and move away slowly.

This projection of love will probably not work on all animals. Discretion is definitely the better part of valor when it comes to dealing with animals. And always send love and thanks back to the animal.

Chapter Eleven

Indigo Children

The next topic that we've chosen for discussion, is Indigo children. Many books have been written to date on this subject, and in my opinion there is a very strong misunderstanding being published in much of this printed material. And that is the assumption that every child being born right now is an Indigo child. Indigo children have actually been being born for the last forty-five or fifty years and even beyond. An Indigo child is a child that is born without prejudice; a child of the new age. It is a child that is loved, and loves it's fellow beings. It is a child that will do just about anything for you with a loving attitude, but if you get belligerant with the child and try to force a situation, the child will resist you.

Indigo children are extremely physchic and very intuitive. They are sensative to the world around them and sense other people's feelings as being their own. Unable to pull apart from other people's feelings, they will cry when the mother or father cries and often wonder why people treat each other harshly. They have extremely loving abilities, and unlike many children, they are neither selfish nor self-centered. They are loving and kind and want everyone to be in harmony. This ability to "feel" what others around them are feeling can sometimes makes it difficult for Indigo Children to determine where "feelings" are coming from, from others or feelings in themselves.

An Indigo child is extremely responsive to love, and loves people very much. It doesn't matter to them the color of a person skin or what religion a person is. These children actually love and accept anothers for exactly who they are.

Indigo children are very curious daydreamers. It is hard for them to learn in a classroom if they think the teacher doesn't like them, and they can become very emotionally distraught if they feel their mother or father is disappointed in them. They have a high level of intelligence and learn very quickly; however, they can also become bored easily.

An Indigo child is not a violent child, nor will they hurt another person. I often read articles that state Indigo children are overly agressive and that this agression is normal. This agression is not normal and is not typical of an Indigo child.

If you believe you may have an Indigo child based on this behavior, it may simply be because of a chemical imbalance or other problem in the child's physical makeup. You might correct this by taking the child off certain sugars and red and yellow dyes. The chemicals in these products have a definite affect on the brain. You should also move the child's Seratonin level up intuitively to the level that is correct for that child's age group. Do not be fooled by thinking the child's tantrums, fits, and rages that cause them to break things, is a sign of an Indigo child. This is a sign of a child that is chemically imbalanced.

I am shocked by children who come into my office and destroy everything that they touch, while their mothers politely explain that they are Indigo children. Indigo children do not have a desire to destroy everything in their path.

Do not be mistaken by the youthfulness of children and call them Indigo to excuse their abnormal behaviors. Indigo children are loving normal children. Many of the people that are born right now, who are healing on the earth, have been born Indigo children.

An Indigo child is not always a "know it all", that's a personality trait. A truly authentic sign of an Indigo child, is a child that loves without prejudice, that serves and loves the parents because they love them, who in turn teaches the parent how to be a parent, and speaks up for injustices. If the parents discipline them unfairly, they will tell them. They will say that isn't fair, or that it's not right, and they are stubborn in their belief systems.

They know what is right, they believe in it, and they stick up for it. They remind me of little old wise men, housed in little bodies. Be careful when you use the word Indigo children, most of the children on the earth right now have Indigo traits, but if the child is disruptive and/or abusive, they probably have a chemical imbalance, and the child's behavior should not be condoned by defining it as an Indigo child.

The real blessing of these wonderful Indigo spirits is that they have come to our earth to teach us the basics of true unconditional love.

Indigo children become remarkably intuitive at a very young age, able to see guardian angels and spirits, and as they grow and gather more intuition, they have many spiritual experiences. You must guide these children to learn to use their intuition wisely.

It is said that Indigo's polarity is imbalanced; that it is reversed. It is interesting to note that when people do these reading techniques, their polarity switches also. Anytime you are working or healing in a person's body, your polarity shifts.

These children are intuitive children. Do not mess with the abilities they have been born with. Indigos switch polariaty back and forth all the time. Learn child behaviors and do not medicate your children for just being a child.

Chapter Twelve

Soul Mates

Let's talk about a subject that nearly everyone has an interest in: Soul Mates. Since 1998 I have seen more soul mates find each other than at any other time in history. Because of the electromagnetic pull of the earth, the different shifts, and the spiritual development we are attaining, it is a time when we are beginning to actually love ourselves.

When you can truly love yourself, you're ready for a soul mate. Many people are confused by the phrase "soul mate". Most of this confusion is caused because there is more than one soul mate for each person on the earth.

When asking the Creator for a soul mate, make sure you don't just ask the Creator for a soul mate, or you will be given a soul mate that may not be compatible to you.

A soul mate is anyone that you have known from some other place in time; the pre-existence before time. These soul mates are sometimes compatible and sometimes not, but your heart will love them. Always be specific when asking the creator for a soul mate, and ask for one that is compatible to you.

A soul mate has a magnetic pull that makes your heart beat faster and your palms sweaty.

Some people are confused and ask the Creator for a twin flame. A twin flame is someone who is exactly like you, and unless you really truly like yourself, most people will not find this match compatible.

A soul mate can make you happy, or tear you apart, depending on how you feel about yourself. As I said before, if you truly love yourself, then you're ready for a soul mate. If you have not arrived at a point in time when you can truly love yourself, a soul mate will take you and drag you through the coals; so loving yourself is vital.

As soon as you commence to love yourself there is an interesting energy that opens in the heart chakra. It also triggers your sexual chakra; which also calls to your soul mate. When you begin to call for your soul mate, you will find that you draw other people to you who are attracted to your energy. Not everyone that is going to be attracted to you is a soul mate.

Soul mates have something special inside. Your heart is excited to see them, and you can't wait to see them again. Part of our evolution as human

beings is to learn to accept others for who and how they are. And it is very important is that you do not romanticize so much about a partner that you don't see them for who they are.

It is imperative when you find your soul mate, that you accept this person for who he/she is, and if they are cooperative and get along with you, and understand and agree with what you believe is right and wrong.

As I previously stated, I've seen more people find soul mates in this point in time than at any other time in history that I am aware of. An interesting side effect of all this, is that in the same period of time , I've also watched numerous marriages simply break up after thirty years or more because both partners suddenly find their true soul mates.

Soul mates are part of the evolution of the earth. As partners we will go up and change together.   As healers we can help bring forth the right partners who will walk with us and stay by us through life.

 Another specific request of the Creator is to ask that you find a soul mate who you can actually grow with you. This will allow you to be able to grow together, so one doesn't outgrow the other. When you're looking for a soul mate and checking out the programs of another person, you should check to see if he/she believes that they can be loved by another person, and if he/she can receive love from another person.

These programs should be present in the other person for them to be your perfect soul mate. I would advise you to muscle check for these things, and make the necessary changes for both of you to give and receive love.

Many people are givers and have a tendency to give all the time, and they will draw soul mates to them that are actually takers. Be certain that you are ready for a soul mate to give you back the love that you give. Always make sure that you can accept and receive joy, and that you can accept and receive love when looking for a soul mate.

When others come to you who are looking for their soul mate and they seem to be going in circles, make sure that they are clear of these programs.

You will find that some people have the subconscious program that there is no one out there for them. And I see women all the time that say, "There is nothing out there but rotten men." And all they ever find is rotten men. And then again there is men who come to me and they are saying, "There is nothing out there but women who use men," and that's all they find. Your subconscious will bring to you what it is told to bring.

If you want a compatible mate, then know precisely what you're looking for; know what qualifications you are looking for in a person. Know if this person is kind and loving and good,and if this person can grow with you. Make that as a prerequisite for your subconscious. Then make sure that a person who is looking for the right mate has the correct program of finding someone that will love in return as much as they love themselves.

Also check them for the program that love hurts, and remove that program, and replace it with what the Creator tells you to replace it with, something like, "love is good for me," and so forth. It is very important that you bring to you the right mate to walk with you through life in this part of our existence, so we can continue to grow.

A soul mate compliments you. Only after you learn to love yourself will you find a soul mate. No person can not make you complete; you must first be complete on your own. If you are not complete first, then you have nothing to bring to the table, so to speak. One of you will take from the other and completely drain that person. Be extremely careful when you ask for a soul mate that you know exactly what you are asking for and will recognize that person when you find him/her.

There is a lot of controversy evolving around whether or not a person can love more than one person. I believe that a person can definitely love more than one person. But, I also believe that the higher evolution of a being is to love one person totally and completely. Actually, to say that you love more than one person is a kind of cop out, because then you're not obligated to knowing a person completely and wholly, and understanding them and comitting to them as a partner.

After working with thousands of people, I have discovered that there is a gene for monogamy, as well as a gene for non-monogamy. It is not ours to judge, no matter who a person finds as a partner. However, it is important to

know that soul mates are out there and are very likely searching for you. Good luck in finding the perfect soul mate for your life's journey. And if you've already found one, good luck in learning to know and understanding this person.

Chapter Thirteen

Manifesting

Everything that we do and everything that we say is reflected by what we are manifesting in our lives. Every decision we make is also reflected by what we are manifesting in our life as well. If we only paid more attention to what we were thinking or what we were saying, we would make our manifestations more of what we wanted.

When deciding what it is you want to manifest in your life, the biggest problem is deciding what it is that you truly want. Many people don't know what they want in their life, therefore they can never create it. And some people believe that their life is leading them and they are not leading their life, so they go with the flow and wait to see what happens.

The truth is that we are creating our own reality, and that may be a hard pill to swallow, but it is the truth none the less. If you can decide to concentrate, really concentrate, on what you want in your life, you can use one of two manifesting techniques that really work, and have proven themselves time and time again.

One was shown to me about six years ago from the Creator when I went up and asked a question on whether I could see truth. Not only was I shown that we create our own realities, but I was shown truth about many people's live's. One of the biggest truths I was shown was how we have the ability to change our own reality.

To do this you need to imagine yourself going up above your space and looking down at your life as if you were in a bubble, or a plastic dome of some sort. Looking down at your life, visualize yourself going about doing all the things you want to do and having all the possession, or whatever, that you could ever desire having, and being peaceful and happy. From this position, high above yourself, you make the command, "I command this in my life now." You do this as we instructed in doing the healings and readings:

1. "Father, Mother, God.
2. I command
3. *(What it is that you want manifested)

4. Thank-you.

5. It is done, it is done, it is done."

Then you imagine that you are a tall, giant person, reaching your arm down into your life as you go about your business, stirring up the energy in your life, and saying, "This is in my life now, and so it is." As you stir up the energy, (you stir it up two or three times around) imagine yourself coming back up, moving your arm up out of the dome, rinsing yourself off, and putting yourself back into your space.

This way of manifesting is phenomenal, and deserves that you do it several times before you make a decision as to how it works. What you decide to manifest in your life, can and will come true.

Another manifesting technique, which is actually fun, and also a great experience, is the Kahuna Mana manifestation. The Hawaiian Kahunas believe that your higher self manifested your physical self; that something is not made of nothing. So they would gather the mana energy, the life force, around them and send it up to the higher self to create what they wanted to create.

To begin this manifesting exercise (technique) choose something that you wish to manifest in your life.

Manifesting Technique. Prior to commencing, have in mind the object or situation you have chosen to manifest in you life. To commence, you will need to sit down with your legs uncrossed and become very relaxed. Expel all the air from your lungs. Do this by exhaling the air from the lungs, literally forcing our more air by using short exhaling puffs. This removes all of the old air from the lungs, making room for a large amount of mana.

Take a deep breath, taking it in all the way and pushing the air deep into the belly, (ballooning the belly) and hold for thirty (30) seconds. If you are a woman this is all you do before you release the breath. If you are a man, you take another breath in (before exhaling the belly breath) to fill up the chest. In mana energy, the life force is held in the stomach for the woman and in the chest for the man. Hold the breath for thirty (30) seconds and then release . Take in another deep breath and push the air deep into the belly (men need to take another inhalation, same as before) hold for thirty (30) seconds and

release. As you hold the air, you imagine the Mana, the life force energy, going through your body and nourishing every cell as light. As you release the air the second time, you take a third deep breath in doing exactly the same as before (with men taking another inhalation to fill up the chest) holding for thirty (30) seconds and releasing. On the fourth breath, place your hands our in front of you as though you were holding a ball and imaagine a ball of energy is being built up between your hands as you take the next deep breath in and push it down into the belly (and of course if you are a man, taking another inhalation to fill up the chest),hold for thirty (30) seconds and release.

As you take in the next deep breath, feel the energy building stronger and stronger. Imagine this ball of light growing. Push the air into the belly (extra inhalation for the men to fill up the chest) and hold for thirty (30) seconds and release. On the sixth and final breath, take a deep breath in, push the air into the belly (men/extra inhalation to fill up chest) hold for thirty (30) seconds and as you near completion of holding the breath, imagine the ball of energy going into the solar plexis, up through your heart, through your throat, up through your crown chakra and about six feet above your head.

At this time you command the energy by saying, "I have this in my life now, Thank you. It is done, it is done." This command can be made while holding the breath or if you find it necessary to exhale during the command, that is acceptable. It is very important to send a picture to your subconscious of exactly what you have chosen to manifest.

Sending a picuture to your higher self tells the higher self what you want in your life. Command it to be so and so it is, now. When you have finished, rinse yourself off and put yourself back into your space. This Hawaiian Kahuna technique is especially efficient, and has many magnificient qualities.

Some very important points to remember when you are manifesting, is that you can not manifest someone to love you. No matter how much you want this, you can not make someone love you; that is their own free will. You're only allowed to manifest what is happening in your life. You are not allowed to manifest for others. You can not manifest for your spouse to get a job; you can only manifest what you want for you.

You could also use this technique to manifest new guides in your life. However, when manifesting new guides in your life, always ask for a guide that is more intelligent than you are, but not so intelligent that you can't understand what they're saying.

Use these strong manifesting techniques with wisdom and joy. Understand that we can manifest our life. Manifesting in theta means that the chances of getting what you have chosen to manifest for, are extremely high, about eighty to ninety percent. Just talking about things will sometimes manifest things in your life, and chances of that happening are about thirty to forty percent, visualizing increases your chances nearer to fifty percent. But going into theta increases the manifestations enormously.

Creating in theta is very powerful; remember that theta is a creative wave. This should be a reminder when contemplating different things that can take our brain into theta. Sometimes as children play video games, their brain waves slip into theta. If you have observed your children playing their video games, you've probably noticed that they are in an almost complete trance state. Be cautious of what you allow your children to view and hear when you allow them tapes and games that display destrucive material, so that you are not training their subconscious to be destructive in the future.

One important thing to remember when you are doing any kind of manifesting is that you will get exactly what you ask for. Always ask for the highest and the best. If you need money, lets say you need ten thousand dollars, be mindful that you ask for it in the highest and the best way, otherwise your ten thousand dollars may be from an accident insurance claim filed on behalf of yourself. Again, always make sure it is in the highest and the best, and always be specific in what you want, because the Creator will always give you exactly what you ask for!

Use these techniques with caution, because they are powerful. Use them with wisdom and use them with joy.

Chapter Fourteen

My Little Story

For years I dreamed of a man that I was to be with later on in my life. I knew that he would have brown hair and blue eyes. As time passed, I knew that this person would be from Montana. I knew that he was a rancher or/and a farmer; I couldn't decide which one it would be, but I knew that it was one of the two, and I knew that he would have a child. When I first dreamed about him, I knew that he was already married, but that he would become divorced.

As time drew near for our first meeting, I knew that he would be driving an old blue and white truck and I knew that he had a son. And in the dreams I would try to reach this boy to have him tell his father that I was coming. I would dream that I had turned into a wolf and would run into the boy's dreams. Waking the boy, I would try and give him a signal that I was coming to see his father someday. The boy would wake up screaming and crying. It wasn't until years later, in 1997, that I met this man.

From my dreams I would always call him my guy from Montana. I asked the Creator time and time again what his name was, but I was told simply that he was my guy from Montana. In 1997 I met a man whose name was Guy. Guy was a farmer and a rancher, or rather he farmed on his parent's farm in Idaho, or he worked on their ranches in Montana and Idaho. He told me that his son had dreamt for a long time about wolves that kept coming into his dreams and waking him up. I had seen this man in such detail that when I met him, I thought the Creator was playing a joke on me, for certainly it couldn't be this easy.

To this day I know that the Creator gives you all the answers you need. I used to go up and ask the Creator the name of this person, and I would get, "He's your guy." My husband's name is Guy and he is from Montana. He is a partner with me on this journey, supporting me completely, as we travel to different places in the world teaching people.

I pray that you will listen to what the Creator tells you. I pray that you will know that the answers you get are clear and real. I pray that you will be able to keep what is called your egotism out of this equation. If you can keep your ego out of this process, the part of you that doesn't want to listen to what is true will not be allowed to enter it's own interpretation. I pray that you will listen to what God says, it's that simple.

And it is my sincere hope that you have found this book helpful to you in your everyday life and I pray that you share this new found knowledge with others and most of all may you come to know that between you and the Creator, no challenge is impossible. Remember the Creator answers your questions. Sometimes the questions are answered very simply. The last story was dedicated to my husband, and also to remind you that the Creator speaks in subtle terms.

Concerning the programming, when you doubt your own healing abilities, pull those self doubts. Any doubt or fear will block you from becoming the healer that you are. When you pull old beliefs, replace them with the knowing that God is the healer. Knowing and living are sometimes two different things. If you live knowing that God is the healer, miracles will happen around you, and everything in your life will change.

For further information about schedules

for DNA classes or activations, call

(208) 524-0808

Vianna

Natures Path

2100 Niagara

Idaho Falls, ID 83404

email: vianna@srv.net

web site: www.thetahealing.com

A
Acetaldehyde, 88, 89, 107, 123
Acidophilus, 125
Acne, 100
Affirmations, 50
Aids, 124, 125
Alcoholism, 107
Allergies, 107
Aloe Vera, 125
Alpha, 8, 16, 21, 23, 29
Aluminum, 89, 91
Alzheimer's, 87
Amalgam, 84, 87, 88, 91
Amino Acids, 82, 95, 101, 108
Anemia, 100, 107
Angels, 12, 133, 134, 146
Apple Juice, 125
Arsenic, 91
Arthritis, 100, 106
Asbestos, 89, 90
Asthma, 107, 108
Auditory Sense, 23
Aura, 12, 129

B
Bacteria, 94
Bar Berry, 125
Bee Pollen, 125
Belief System, 10, 34, 37, 39, 40, 41, 42, 46, 47, 58, 62, 65, 68, 70, 72, 73,
　　　　　74, 75, 76, 146
Beta, 8, 23
Beta Carotene, 93
Bilberry, 126
Biopsy, 6, 7
Birth Defects, 100
Black Cohosh, 126
Black Walnut, 122, 126

Index

Bladder Infection, 108
Bleeding Gums, 108
Block on Healing, 65, 74
Blood Disorders, 108
Blue-Green Algae, 89
Body, 18, 78, 79, 81, 104
Boron, 100, 106
Bowel Disorder, 108
Broken Bones, 109
Bronchitis, 93
Burdock Root, 126

C
Camu, 126
Cadmium, 91
Calcium, 24, 93, 97, 100, 101, 106, 109, 112, 115, 116, 120, 122
Cancer, 6, 26, 29, 34, 35, 36, 50, 64, 71, 94, 99, 100, 103, 104, 105, 106, 125
Candida, 88, 100, 109, 123
Carbon Monoxide, 89
Carcinogen, 99
Carpal Tunnel, 95, 96, 109
Carrot Juice, 126
Cascara Sagrada, 126
Cataract, 95, 114
Catnip, 126
Cats Claw, 126
Cayenne Pepper, 91, 126
Chakras, 24, 69, 110, 133, 149
Chamomile, 126
Chaparral, 126
Chelated Minerals, 98
Chemical Reaction, 51
Chinese Ma Hung, 126
Chlorella, 90, 91, 126
Chromium, 99, 100, 101, 112
Chromosome(s), 9, 10, 27, 46, 47, 107, 112
Clips, 78, 79, 80, 81, 108, 113
Colon Cancer, 36
Colon Disorders, 110, 125
Collective Consciousness, 52

Index

Coma, 110
Conscious Mind, 41, 65
Copper, 89, 100
CoQ10, 100, 101, 123, 126
Core Belief, 11, 40, 41, 46, 57, 60, 61, 63, 68, 83, 84, 106, 112, 113
Coriander, 87, 91, 120
Creative Force, 8
Creator, 3, 5, 7, 11, 12, 13, 16, 18, 21, 22, 26, 28, 29, 30, 32, 36, 37, 40, 43,
      47, 48, 50, 54, 55, 60, 65, 66, 67, 68, 78, 80, 81, 82, 87, 101, 107,
      110, 111, 112, 113, 115, 116, 122, 123, 129, 137, 138, 140, 149,
      151, 159, 160
Crown Chakra, 7, 16, 18, 24, 30, 110, 133

D
Damiana, 120, 126
Dandelion Root, 126
DDT, 89
Deafness, 111
Death Wish, 111
Delta, 8
Dehydrated, 42, 43, 44
Depression, 76, 82, 83, 84, 87, 112, 125
Diabetes, 9, 26, 100, 112
Diarrhea, 87
Dizziness, 113
DNA, 9, 10, 27, 46, 47, 49, 69, 78, 79, 82, 90, 111, 124
DNA Activation, 9
Double Helix, 46

E
Echinacea, 127
Electroencephalograph, 8
Electromagnetic Field, 20, 44, 149
Emotions, 34, 37, 47, 51, 63, 79, 106, 114, 122, 130
Emphatic Sense, 23
Endocrine System, 113
Etheric Field, 52
Evolution, 9, 150
Eyes, 113
Eyesight, 81

Index

Fat Gene, 160
Farsighted, 79, 114
Feelings, 37, 50, 51, 78, 79, 81, 122, 130,145
Fenugreek, 127
Fever Few, 127
Femur, 6
Fiberic Tumor, 115
Flax Seed Oil, 127
Folic Acid, 96
Future Body, 78, 79, 80

G
Gallbladder-Liver Cleanse, 115, 118
Gallstones, 115
Garlic Powder, 127
Gene, 13, 46, 47, 50, 51, 69, 81, 113, 151
Generations, 47
Gene Replacement, 46, 77, 78, 80, 112
Genetic, 11, 12, 51, 56, 57, 59, 80, 82, 84, 85, 111
Genetic Beliefs, 37, 57, 68, 106
Genetic Defects, 46, 78, 82, 84, 85, 111
Genetic Level, 41, 46, 47, 50, 56, 58, 61, 62, 66, 81, 82, 83, 107, 114
Genetic Programming, 46, 48, 90
Ginger Root, 127
Ginkgo Biloba, 127
Glaucoma, 114
God, 2, 3, 5, 6, 7, 16, 17, 21, 24, 27, 29, 37, 38, 44, 45, 48, 53, 55, 57,
    58, 61, 64, 65, 66, 67, 68, 69, 71, 72, 73, 74, 75, 76, 79, 80, 82,
    84, 90, 109, 113, 114, 115, 129, 130, 133, 134, 135, 137, 138,
    139, 140, 160
God's Light, 44, 48, 49, 52, 53, 54, 56, 61, 63, 64, 69, 78, 112
Goiter, 101
Golden Seal, 127
Grape Seed Extract, 127
Green Tea, 127
Grid System 137, 138
Group Consciousness, 52
Group Healing, 29
Guarana, 127

Index

H
Hair Loss, 101
Hate, 50, 57, 63, 64, 65, 68, 71, 72, 74, 104
Healed, 34, 63, 80, 105
Healer, 6, 28, 35, 63, 65, 66, 67, 103, 133
Healings, 12, 14, 25, 26, 28
Healing Technique, 11, 13, 15, 26, 27, 32, 38, 48
Heart, 115, 149
Hepatitis, 115
Heavenly Father, 16
Heavy Metal, 34, 104
History Belief/Level, 11, 37, 41, 52, 53, 54, 55, 56, 59, 68, 69, 113
HIV, 124
Hormones, 113
Hydrated, 42, 43, 57, 120
Hypoglycemia, 93, 101, 116
Hypothalamus, 113

I
Immune System, 51, 100, 101, 128
Implants, 136, 140, 141
Incontinence, 116
Indigo Child, 145, 146, 147
Insomnia, 116
Insulin, 112
Instinctual Senses, 23
Instinctual Shamanism, 23
Intuition, 23
Intuitive, 62, 145
Irish Moss, 127

K
Kahuna Energy Break, 20
Kahuna Mana (Manifestation), 151
Kava Kava, 127
Kelp, 127
Kidneys, 116
Knees, 117

L

Ladder, 46
Lead, 89, 91
Lead Poisoning, 89
Leukemia, 119
Life Force, 130
Licorice, 127
Light, 133, 138, 156
Light Therapy, 35
Liver, 63, 105, 117
Liver Cleanse, 87, 91, 115, 116, 121, 123
Love, 28, 29, 44, 51, 71, 72, 76, 143, 145, 149, 150, 151, 156
Lungs, 120

M

Maca, 50, 127
Magnesium, 97, 100, 106, 108, 112, 113, 120
Manifesting, 153, 154, 155
Marshmallow, 128
Master Cell, 49, 81
Master Gland, 49
Medical Intuitive, 5
Memories, 78, 79, 81
Menopause, 12, 127
Menstrual Cramps, 101, 120
Mercury, 34, 87, 91, 99, 119, 120, 126
Mercury Poisoning, 6, 34, 84, 87, 119
Metabolism, 95, 96
Migraine Headaches, 121
Milk Thistle, 116, 128
Minerals, 6, 89
Molybdenum, 88, 89, 107, 109, 123, 124
Money, 12, 13, 48, 49, 57, 58, 59, 67, 75, 157
Morphogenic Field, 47, 48, 50, 51, 52
MS, 26, 100
MSM, 108, 109
Muscle Testing, 41, 42, 57, 106

N
Nearsighted, 79, 81, 114
Neurons, 44, 112
Noradrenalin, 51, 84
Nucleic Acid, 46, 47

O
Oath, 52, 53, 54, 58,
Obesity, 121
Olive Leaf Extract, 123, 128
Oregano, 128
Osteoporosis, 122

P
Panthothetic Acid, 96
Parasites, 122, 123, 125, 126
Parkinson's, 87
Parsley, 128
Peppermint Leaves, 128
Pesticides, 89
Phantom Strands, 9
Pineal Gland, 49, 81
Pleurisy, 123
PMS, 101, 121
Poison, 85, 86, 117
Potassium, 99, 100, 101, 120
Practitioner, 15, 28, 29, 31, 42, 67, 133
Prophetic, 23, 24
Psychic, 84, 145
Psychic Break, 19, 23
Psychic Healings, 84, 106, 129
Psychic Hooks, 139, 140
Psychic Sense, 23, 24
Pumpkin Seed, 91, 128

R
Reading, 5, 12, 14, 15, 19, 20, 23, 31, 44, 48, 134, 135
Receptors, 103, 111, 112
Red Clover, 128

Retina, 82, 114
Rickets, 93
RNA, 125
Royal Camu, 112

S
Safflower Powder, 128
Saw Palmetto, 128
Selenium, 87, 91, 99, 100, 101, 124
Self Love, 72
Seratonin, 51, 83, 84, 107, 112, 116, 117
Sexual Disfunction, 101
Sexual Stimulation, 101
Shadow Chromosomes, 10
Shamanism, 23
Shipper, 47
Siberian Ginseng, 128
Sinus, 123
Skin Problems, 123
Slippery Elm, 128
Solar Plexus, 23,
Soul Fragments, 54, 139
Soul Level, 37, 41, 54, 55, 58, 62, 68, 112
Soul Mates, 149, 150, 151, 152
Source, 3, 7, 10, 22, 69
Spirits, 137, 138, 146
Spirulina, 90
St. John's Wort, 112
Stroke, 124
Subconscious, 12, 15, 20, 21, 22, 25, 26, 27, 40, 41, 44, 45, 46, 50,
                51, 61, 62, 68, 80, 82, 105, 107, 113, 129, 151, 157
T
Telomeres, 10, 90
Teeth, 124
Theta, 8, 9, 21, 23, 26, 27, 29, 84, 130, 157
Third Eye, 23, 24, 49
Thyroid Cancer, 35
Tocophorol, 94
Toxicity, 93, 98, 99
Toxins, 26, 34, 37, 51, 85, 86, 87, 90, 103, 104, 108, 117
Truth, 59, 154

U
Ulcers, 125
Unconditional Love, 27, 29, 146
Universal Source, (See God, Creator, Source)

V
Valerian Root, 128
Venereal Disease, 124
Viral Infection, 124
Viruses, 100, 103, 108
Vitamins
—Vitamin A, 93
—Vitamin B1, 94
—Vitamin B2, 95, 100
—Vitamin B3, 95
—Vitamin B6, 35, 100
—Vitamin B12, 96
—Vitamin C, 91, 100, 108
—Vitamin D, 93
—Vitamin E, 91, 93, 100, 120, 124
—Vitamin K, 94

W
Waywards, 136, 137, 138, 139
White Oak Bark, 128
White Willow Bark, 128
Window of Light, 137

Y
Yellow Dock Root, 128
Yucca Root, 139
Zinc, 89, 98, 100, 101, 106
Zipping UP, 20

Notes

Notes